A HANDBOOK OF LOGIC

A Handbook of Logic.

by Joseph Gerard Brennan
BARNARD COLLEGE, COLUMBIA UNIVERSITY

HARPER & BROTHERS, PUBLISHERS, NEW YORK

A Handbook of Logic
Copyright © 1957, by Harper & Brothers
Printed in the United States of America
All rights in this book are reserved.

L-G

Library of Congress catalog card number: 57–8062

To Catherine

Contents

Preface

Some say that the purpose of logic books is to teach people "how to think." Now logic books are usually written by logicians, and if it were true that logic teaches people how to think, one would suppose that logicians themselves would be expert thinkers and would make no mistakes (or at least very few). And if *this* were so, all logicians would be rich men. But, alas, that is not the case.

Why not simply say that a first book of logic should serve to acquaint us with some principles and problems of inference, deductive and inductive? That is enough to justify any introduction to logic.

Of course, it may well be that logic teaches us to think in the sense that through it we experience a certain useful type of precision. This is the point of Gilbert Ryle's clever analogy between formal logic and military drill: "It is not the stereotyped motions of drill, but its standards of perfection of control which are transmitted from the parade-ground to the battlefield. . . . To know how to go through completely stereotyped movements in artificial parade-ground conditions with perfect correctness is to have learned not indeed how to conduct oneself in battle but how rigorously to apply standards of soldierly efficiency even to unrehearsed actions and decisions in novel and nasty situations and in irregular and unfamiliar country."[1] To Mr. Ryle, the unfamiliar country concealing the novel and nasty situations is philosophy. But it could just as well be any area of human learning—law, medicine, business, pure science—in which the novice would not be the worse for some preliminary exercise in that tidiness of mind which logic exacts.

[1] Ryle, *Dilemmas* (42), pp. 112, 123. (Numbers in parentheses refer to the General Bibliography, p. 213, where details of publication are given.)

This handbook introduces the reader both to the traditional logic of the syllogism and to modern "symbolic" logic. After all, they are not two different logics; the older logic is but a part, although an important part, of the wider realm of modern generalized logic. In addition, there is a brief survey of inductive logic, as well as a look at the traditional fallacies of argument. For the mechanically inclined, there is appended a short section on logical machines, their construction and use in science and industry.

This small book has been a pleasure to write. I am thinking of all those logic classes at the College of New Rochelle and later at Barnard, and the good times we've had. I would like to thank John Cranford Adams, president of Hofstra College, for providing me a pleasant summer space to write in. I am immensely indebted to my colleague on the Barnard faculty, Miss Judith Jarvis, for her careful reading of manuscript and proof, and her invaluable suggestions for revision. My friend Eugene Abrams of Franklin Square, Long Island, made the ingenious syllogism machine described in the appendix.

J. G. B.

June, 1957

A HANDBOOK OF LOGIC

1

What Is Logic?

For the moment, let us say that logic is the study of certain types of *inference*. We may define inference, roughly, as any passing from knowledge to new knowledge. Hearing that a man's name is MacPherson, I may infer or "conclude" (correctly or not) that he is a Scotsman. Hearing a scream from the kitchen, I may infer (rightly or wrongly) that the teakettle is boiling. Informed that $2x = 10$, I may infer that $x = 5$. Observing the rapid fall of the barometer aboard ship, I predict heavy weather ahead. Whenever, taking something to be so, I conclude that something else is so, I infer.

The study of the rules and operations which pertain to certain important kinds of inference is logic. Broadly, the term "logic" may correctly be applied to the systematic study of *any* kind of inference. We use the word in this general sense when we speak of "the logic of modern physics," or "the logic of social science." John Dewey uses "logic" in the comprehensive sense of a general theory of inquiry. More strictly—and this is the sense in which logic is taken when we think of it as an exact science—logic is the study of certain types of deductive inference.

Deductive and Inductive Inference

The difference between deduction and induction is this: In deduction, the connection between a given piece of information and another piece of information concluded from it is a *necessary* connection. In a valid deductive argument, if the premises are true, the conclusion *must* be true. If no ballet dancers are wooden-legged men, then it *necessarily follows* that no wooden-legged men are ballet dancers. If $2x = 10$, then it *must* be that x = 5. Suppose I am told that the number of Vassar girls is greater than the number of days in the year. I may conclude *with certainty* that there are at least two Vassar girls who have the same birthday. At first sight, it may appear that such an inference is at best probable, since it seems directly to concern the properties of natural objects and events (Vassar girls and days). Closer inspection shows us, however, that the inference depends only on *the connection between the ideas* in statement A, "The number of Vassar girls is greater than the number of days in the year," and statement B, "There are at least two Vassar girls with the same birthday." Let us *suppose* the truth of statement A; as formal logicians, we need not verify its factual or material truth. To establish the inference as deductive, we need only ask: *does* the truth of the second statement *therefore* follow? It does. The first statement *logically implies* the second, just as "X is greater than Y and Y is greater than Z" logically implies "X is greater than Z."

In *induction,* on the other hand, the connection between an item of information and another item inferred from it is *not* a logically necessary connection. From observation of very many Siamese cats, I conclude that all such cats have blue eyes. But this inductive conclusion is not necessarily contained in the information that all Siamese cats so far observed have been blue-eyed. Or suppose that as astronomers we have looked at a large number of comets, and have noted that each moves in an elliptical orbit. Suppose further that no observed comet has failed to move in such an orbit. Now such data may give us very good reason for concluding that all comets move in elliptical orbits; yet this conclusion, reached by induction, is not logically implied by the information at hand. For, from the information that all previously *observed* comets move in elliptical orbits it does not *necessarily follow* that *all* comets move in this way.

What is the distinction between "inference" and "implication"? They are obviously closely related processes. In ordinary discourse, the latter may mean "to give a hint," and the former "to take a hint." Thus when my hostess yawns and looks at the clock I *infer* from her behavior that she would like me to go home. Her yawn and look *imply* that this is her desire. In formal inference, the *statements* "$2x = 10$" and "$y = 2x$" imply the statement that $y = 10$. From the first two statements, *we* infer the statement that $y = 10$. Because of the psychological element in inference, many formal logicians prefer to say that their business is with *implication* rather than inference.

Truth and Validity

Suppose I am informed that the following two statements are true:

Wombats are kind to their children.
Those who are kind to their children occasionally beat them.

I may infer that:

Wombats occasionally beat their children.

The inference is formally correct, though many would object that it is rather silly. It may be true that *materially* the sentences are foolish and even false. But if we *assume* the truth of the first two sentences, the truth of the third "follows." That is, the third statement is formally implied by the first two. Thus, formal inference, and therefore formal logic itself, is not concerned with material truth directly; rather, it is concerned with formal correctness or *validity*.

Material truth has to do with the relation of a sentence to a factual situation. The sentence "Silver is mined in Nevada" is true if in fact silver is mined in Nevada. Validity, on the other hand, concerns forms of sentences and their relations to one another in argument. What is form? One way of identifying it is to say that form is that which remains the same throughout changes in matter or content. Federal income-tax Form 1040 is the same for all who use it, but the *content* written into it by the individual taxpayer differs in each case. Consider the following sentences:

Paris is smaller than Cannes.
Naples is smaller than Paris.

The first statement happens to be materially false, the second true. The content of the first sentence is different from the content of the second. But both are of the same *form*, namely:

> *x* is smaller than *y*.

The letters "*x*" and "*y*" are used here as what the logicians call "*variables*"; that is, they neither name nor designate anything whatever in the way in which the words "Paris," "Cannes," and "Naples" do. They may be considered as nothing but a convenient symbolic device for indicating *blank spaces*, which are to be *filled in* with the names of things. Now when we examine the pair of statements given above, we see that we can conclude (or "deduce") from them that:

> Naples is smaller than Cannes.

This statement is not materially true. But it has correctly been drawn from the other two statements, and this not on the basis of any information we may have regarding the actual size of Paris, Cannes, and Naples, but on the basis of *formal relations* alone.

Similarly, given the conditional statement:

> If the sun is out, then the grass is dry.

we may infer that:

> Either the sun is not out, or the grass is dry.

The validity of this inference depends not on our knowledge of the sun or the weather, but on our knowledge of the connection between certain *sentence forms:*

1. If *p*, then *q*.
2. Either not-*p* or *q*.

In these sentence forms, "*p*" and "*q*" are variables, to be replaced, however, by *sentences* rather than names.

Formal Science

Since it deals with the *forms* of sentences and the connections between them, logic is commonly called a *formal science.* This is another way of saying that formal logic does not deal with questions of empirical fact or material truth. Mathematics too is a formal science, "$\sqrt{4} = 2$" is a statement whose truth is independent of the actual physical properties of objects such as chairs, trees, and the like.

The validity of mathematical operations depends upon the implicit granting of certain *logical* assumptions. That is, the rules of mathematics *presuppose* the more general rules of logic. Of course, we must remember that "mathematics" is a sort of catchall name which includes a number of separate disciplines—arithmetic, geometry, algebra, and so on. "Logic" too—even in the strict sense of deductive logic—applies to a number of systems of exact inference which may differ considerably from one another.

Formal sciences are purely *deductive.* That is, they proceed by means of formal analysis rather than by physical observation, test, and measurement. Those disciplines whose methods *do* include physical observation and experiment we call *empirical* sciences. Now the odd thing is that certain of these sciences, such as theoretical physics, have very little to do with the observation and classifying of physical objects in nature; they deal with unobservable things like atoms and rely heavily on formal (mathematical) inference. Such disciplines as theoretical physics are highly deductive, even if not wholly so. It seems that the more refined and sophisticated a science, the closer is its character to that of a purely formal science. On the other hand, sciences in less advanced stages of development depend more directly on physical description, observation, and classifying; they rely more on "induction" than on "deduction" for their laws. Perhaps we could paraphrase Walter Pater and say, "All science tends toward the condition of mathematics." But it would be necessary to add that mathematics itself aspires to the condition of logic.

Classical or Aristotelian Logic

One type of formal logic is very ancient and has been taught in association with the subject of philosophy for over two thousand years. Four centuries before Christ,

Aristotle wrote the first logic textbook. (Euclid had already written the first geometry textbook.) Through medieval and modern times, logicians developed Aristotle's logic in a very thorough way. Thus developed, logic is variously referred to as "Aristotelian," "traditional," or "classical." But, just as today we know that Euclidean geometry is only *one* kind of geometry, so also do we know that Aristotelian logic is only one kind of formal logic. More accurately, Aristotelian logic concentrates on one system of formal inference. While this system of logic is very interesting (and, as we shall see, a good deal of fun), it is by no means the only system which can be worked out within formal logic.

The pattern of formal inference around which Aristotelian logic is ordered is called the *syllogism*. The logical example above about the wombats (p. 3) is a syllogism. The simplest type of syllogism consists of two statements, called premises, from which follows another statement, called the conclusion:

> Those who war against their neighbors do wrong.
> The Thebans war against their neighbors.
> _____
> Therefore, the Thebans do wrong.

Aristotle clearly pointed out that what the logician is interested in is the *form* rather than the subject matter of this type of inference. In his actual writing, he frequently omits subject matter from his illustrations and gives us only the forms of syllogisms to consider:

> All *A* is *B*.
> All *C* is *A*.
> _____
> All *C* is *B*.

Thus within the limits imposed on it by confinement to syllogistic and allied forms of inference, Aristotle's logic is just as "symbolic" as modern logic, although not nearly so inclusive.

Modern Generalized or "Symbolic" Logic

A little more than one hundred years ago, George Boole, teaching in Ireland, showed that algebra combines easily with logical operations. The Germans E. Schröder, G. Frege, and others then showed how logical systems far more comprehensive than those of classical logic could be constructed. New sets of logical concepts and operations were quickly set up and worked out. In 1910, the Englishmen A. N. Whitehead and Bertrand Russell brought out an encyclopedia of the new comprehensive logic. This great work, the *Principia Mathematica,* showed how to construct a large number of logical systems, each of which revealed some aspect of the foundations of mathematics.

The work of Whitehead and Russell stimulated the production of a large number of logic systems with various schemes of symbolic notations. Today logicians are almost embarrassed by the rich multiplicity of logical systems developed within the framework of symbolic logic. The new logic has been of enormous theoretical importance; its practical application is increasing daily in such widely differing fields as insurance, genetics, and engineering. Logic machines, analogous to mathematical computers (see Appendix) have been successfully constructed and put to work to solve certain technical problems which have arisen in various specialized departments of science and industry.

In this survey, most of our attention will be focused on deductive logic. After analyzing the basic concepts of classical or syllogistic logic, we shall examine certain elements of modern generalized or symbolic logic. Our main enterprise concluded, we shall devote a section to inductive logic, finishing our inquiry with a brief glance at the classical fallacies in argument.

QUESTIONS AND EXERCISES

1. What do we mean when we say of a person that he is "logical"?
2. What is inference? Give five examples of inferences that might be drawn by a person during the course of an ordinary day.

3. Distinguish between inference and implication. Write two sentences showing the correct English usage of the words "infer" and "imply."

4. Distinguish between deductive and inductive inference, giving examples of each.

5.   Cats catch mice.

         <u>Cat is a three-letter word</u>

         ∴ Some three-letter words catch mice.

Show how the order of language and the order of natural objects and events have been confused to produce this absurdity.

6. Distinguish between "truth" and "validity" in simple and clear language, using your own examples.

7. Which of the following conclusions are materially true? Which have been validly drawn?

  1. Some vertebrates are mammals.

    ∴ *Some mammals are vertebrates.*

  2. Most bears wear dungarees.

    ∴ *At least one bear wears dungarees.*

  3. All residents of New York reside in the United States.

    All residents of the Bronx reside in the United States.

    ∴ *All residents of the Bronx are residents of New York.*

  4. All bachelors are unmarried men.

    ∴ *All unmarried men are bachelors.*

  5. Dinosaurs are good house pets.

    Good house pets eat dog biscuits.

    ∴ *Some who eat dog biscuits are dinosaurs.*

  6. *At least one American poet wore a beard,* because Walt Whitman was an American poet and he wore a beard.

8. Examine the following formal inferences, stating which are valid and which are not.

  1. All Bulgarians are Slavs.

    Some residents of Sofia are Slavs.

    ∴ Some residents of Sofia are Bulgarians.

  2. Some redheads are not good-tempered.

    All Buddhist priests are good-tempered.

    ∴ Some Buddhist priests are not redheads.

  3. No bassoon players eat artichokes.

    All who eat artichokes eventually go mad.

    ∴ Some who eventually go mad are not bassoon players.

4. Some cuttlefish registered for library cards.
   None who registered for library cards are old residents.
   ∴ No old residents are cuttlefish.
5. Some anteaters do fine embroidery.
   All who do fine embroidery make good wives.
   ∴ Some who make good wives are anteaters.

9. Which of the two formal inferences below are valid? Explain in each case.
   1. John is the father of Eleanor, and Eleanor is the mother of Clement; therefore, John is the grandfather of Clement.
   2. All mothers love their children; therefore all children love their mothers.

10. What is meant by "formal science"? Why are mathematics and logic called formal sciences?

11. What is an empirical science? Give examples. In what way may empirical sciences use formal science? Explain and illustrate.

12. What is meant by classical or Aristotelian logic? Show the distinction between form and subject matter in the syllogism on p. 6.

13. Aristotle says that the logician is interested in the form rather than the matter of the syllogism. Explain.

14. The following puzzles may be solved by purely formal inference. They may take you a little time, and hence should be considered optional.
    1. Given that politicians lie every time they open their mouths and that nonpoliticians always speak the truth. A, B, and C are talking. A says something we don't quite hear, but it's about his belonging to one of the two classes, politician, nonpolitician. B, who *has* heard, says, "A says he is not a politician." C then says, "A is a politician." How many politicians and how many nonpoliticians are there?
    2. Three men go by turn into a dark closet where hang five hats, three red and two blue. Out they come, each man forbidden to look at his own hat, but permitted to look at the hats of the others in an effort to tell the color of his own. A glances at B and C, and says, "I don't know what color hat I have on." B, who is equally intelligent,

looks around and says, "Nor do I know what color hat I have on." C, who is blind but quite intelligent, says, "I know now what color hat I have on." What color hat was C wearing and how did he figure it out?

3. Given a simple balance scale with two pans, and twelve billiard balls to weigh, one of which is irregular in weight. In three weighings, could you determine which is the irregular ball and whether it is lighter or heavier? How would you go about doing this?

4. Here is a variation on the second puzzle. It is useful in annoying people at parties.

You are traveling through dangerous country inhabited only by two Indian tribes, the Blacks and the Whites. White Indians always tell the truth, while Black Indians always lie. You come to a crossroad where you meet two Indians of tribe unknown. You know that only one of the two roads open to you is safe; the other is dangerous. Now in order to find out which is the safe road, you are allowed to ask each Indian one and only one question, the question to be answered by a yes or no. What are the questions you would ask?

2

The Analysis of Propositions

Meaning of Proposition

By "proposition" is meant (roughly) a declarative sentence. Some logicians distinguish between a proposition and a sentence on the ground that a proposition is *what a sentence asserts* rather than the sentence itself. For example, the three different sentences (1) "It is cold," (2) *"Il fait froid,"* and (3) *"Fa freddo"* assert the same proposition. For our purposes, we shall assume that "sentence" and "proposition" are roughly equivalent, provided that "sentence" is understood to mean a declarative sentence. "Are you going to the beach with Pat?" and "Would to God I were a tender apple blossom!" are not declarative sentences, hence not propositions.

Simple and Compound Propositions

We may make an initial distinction between two types of propositions: *simple,* and *compound.* A simple or "categorical" proposition is equivalent to a simple declarative sentence:

They were doing the muskrat ramble.

Compound propositions include:
1. Conjunctive propositions (". . . and . . ."):

You are beautiful and I love you.

2. Conditional, hypothetical, or implicative propositions ("if . . . then . . ."):

If a wombat is tickled, it will laugh.

3. Disjunctive or alternative propositions ("either . . . or . . ."):

Either Kate was joking or Dan was really ill.

The forms of compound propositions are easily handled with a symbolic notation of the type we shall see in Chapter 6.

Elements of Simple Propositions—Terms

Here are some simple propositions:

All cats are musically inclined.
You are a darling.
Not many dragons play the oboe.
Lake Tahoe is west of Reno.
Thorium is a metal.
Buddha died from eating poisoned mushrooms.

Propositions are relatively complex, and can be analyzed into simpler elements known as *terms*. Classical logic breaks down propositions into two terms only, the *subject* term and the *predicate* term. In the proposition:

All cats are musically inclined.

"cats" is the subject term, and "musically inclined" is the predicate term. The subject term is what the proposition is talking about; the predicate term is that which is said about the subject term. The word "all" in this proposition is a *quantifying* word; quantifiers like "all," "some," "not many," etc., tell us how much or how many of the things designated by the term are being talked about. The word "are" is called the *copula* or coupling word. A copula is a part of the verb "to be" that links subject and predicate terms.

In classical logic, propositions that have copulas are interpreted as asserting a relation of inclusion or exclusion between the subject class or kind and the predicate class. In these types, the copula is clearly visible; the propositions have the form *S-Copula-P*:

The yak is a harmless animal.
Oboe players are madmen.
Your son is not a thief.
Japanese girls are polite conversationalists.

> Griffins are fabulous monsters.
> Mesons are atomic particles.
> Sodium is an element.

Many two-term propositions, however, lack the classical copula, as, for example, the sentence:

> Babies cry.

Such propositions can be thrown into the form "S is P," however, by a dodge common in classical logic. The dodge is to paraphrase such propositions in a way that shows a copula even at the cost of changing the meaning of the proposition a little:

> Babies are things that cry.

When we say "Jeanne plays the violin," we do not *quite* mean "Jeanne is a thing that plays the violin," although for purposes of simple logical exercise there is no harm in paraphrasing the original proposition this way. But now consider the proposition:

> I love you.

This proposition states a kind of relationship which is neither one of class membership nor one of class property between two persons "I" and "you." To force such propositions into the Procrustean bed of the class-copula form always results in something stilted and artificial, such as:

> I am something that loves you.

Or worse:

> I am one of your lovers.

In sum, not all propositions contain the verb "to be." In those that do, "is" *may* designate a relation of class membership:

> The octopus is a mollusc.

But "is" may also be used in ways other than that of class inclusion. It may, on the other hand, attach a *property to* a term; this can be translated rather easily into class-inclusion form. It may also be used to express *identity* ("Hesse is the author of *Steppenwolf*"). It may mean *existence* ("There are angels"). Nor are these all of the several senses of the ambiguous "to be." In its analysis of propositions, however, classical logic tends to focus on that sense of "to be" which stands for a relation of inclusion or exclusion between the subject and predicate classes.

Classical Division of Simple Propositions

In classical logic, simple or "categorical" propositions are classified into six types, of which the first four may be considered basic.

1. UNIVERSAL AFFIRMATIVE	(A)	All Hawaiians are good swimmers.
2. UNIVERSAL NEGATIVE	(E)	No Spartans are cowards.
3. PARTICULAR AFFIRMATIVE	(I)	Some Javanese are expert dancers.
4. PARTICULAR NEGATIVE	(O)	Some Italians do not love music.
5. SINGULAR AFFIRMATIVE		Eisenhower is a native of Texas.
6. SINGULAR NEGATIVE		This orangutan is not a typist.

For the sake of brevity, traditional usage refers to the first four propositions by the code letters A, E, I, and O respectively. These code letters are derived from the first and second vowels of the Latin *affirmo* (I affirm) and *nego* (I deny).

Euler Diagrams of Categorical Propositions

The diagrams of propositions invented by the eighteenth-century mathematician L. Euler are still used today, although variations of these, known as the Venn diagrams, are more accurate in representing the structures of the classical propositions. We shall look at both types of diagrams. In the Euler diagrams, each proposition is represented by two circles, each circle representing a class. Negative class labels are excluded; we cannot draw a circle and label it "no cats." Indeed there is no need to, for "not-cats" is everything outside the "cat" circle.

1. Universal Affirmative (A) Proposition

All Hawaiians are good swimmers.

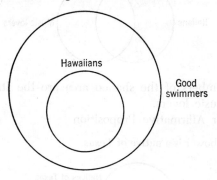

2. Universal Negative (E) Proposition

No Spartans are cowards.

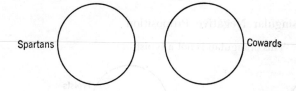

3. Particular Affirmative (I) Proposition

Some Javanese are expert dancers.

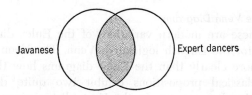

The members of the shaded area are the Javanese who are expert dancers.

4. Particular Negative (O) Proposition

Some Italians are not music lovers.

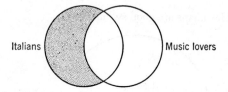

The members of the shaded area are the Italians who are not music lovers.

5. Singular Affirmative Proposition

Eisenhower is a native of Texas.

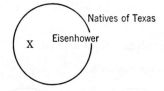

6. Singular Negative Proposition

This orangutan is not a typist.

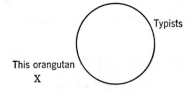

The Venn Diagrams

These are modern variations of the Euler diagrams, named for the English logician J. Venn. The Venn circles show more clearly than the Euler diagrams how the four basic classical propositions exhibit two quite different propositional structures. In the Venn diagrams, each one of the four propositional types (A, E, I, O) is represented by two intersecting circles. The significance of the shaded portion of the Venn circles differs from that of the Euler circles. For in the Venn circles, the shaded area represents that part of the class *which has no members.* When an asterisk or "x" appears, it means "There is at least one member of this area or part of the class." Here are the four main Venn diagrams:

1. Universal Affirmative (A) Proposition

All sardines are friendly.

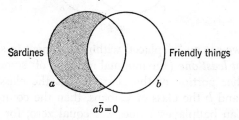

$$a\bar{b} = 0$$

Here the shaded area (nonfriendly sardines) has no members. If *a* stands for the class of sardines, and $\bar{b}$ for the class of whatever is nonfriendly, then our proposition states that the combined class or class *product* (nonfriendly sardines) is equal to zero or null. For there are *no* sardines that are *not* friendly. Thus the symbolic formula for the A proposition is $a\bar{b} = 0$.

2. Universal Negative (E) Proposition

No sinners are saints.

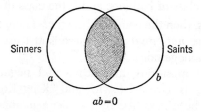

$$ab = 0$$

The area reserved for sinners who are saints has no members. If *a* is the class of sinners, and *b* the class of saints, then the common members of the classes *ab* (that is, sinners who are saints) is zero or null. Hence the formula for this type of proposition is $ab = 0$.

3. Particular Affirmative (I) Proposition

Some ballplayers are Cubans.

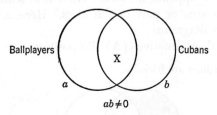

$$ab \neq 0$$

Here we see an "x" placed within a segment to show that there is *at least one* (the minimal meaning of "some") member of that portion of the class. If a is the class of ballplayers, and b the class of Cubans, then the common class ab (Cuban ballplayers) does *not* equal zero, for it has at least one member.

4. Particular Negative (O) Proposition

Some badgers are not monogamous.

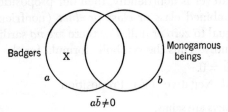

$$a\bar{b} \neq 0$$

If a is the class of badgers, and b the class of all who are monogamous, then the combined class $a\bar{b}$ (nonmonogamous badgers) does *not* equal zero. There is at least one badger who is not monogamous.

Singular propositions, affirmative and negative, of the type "Cannes is a resort town," and "King Kong is not a rabbit," can be diagramed by the Venn method only in a rather awkward fashion. For the Venn diagrams are tailored to show the relations between two *classes*, while the subject terms of the singular propositions do not designate classes but individuals. We have seen that such propositions may be diagramed Euler-fashion.

What about propositions of the type "The elephant is

the only animal with a trunk," or "Only the brave deserve the fair"? The usual way of handling these propositions à la Venn is to transpose the subject and predicate terms and to treat the result as an A proposition. Thus "Only Ulstermen are Orangemen" becomes "All Orangemen are Ulstermen," and may be diagramed according to the Venn scheme for A propositions:

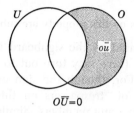

$$O\overline{U}=0$$

Here the U circle is for Ulstermen and the O circle for Orangemen. Since Orangemen who are not Ulstermen are a class of no members, the formula is $O\overline{U} = 0$.

Venn Diagrams and Existential Import of Propositions

When propositions are analyzed according to the Venn diagrams, we may see an important difference in structure in the case of the universal or general (A and E) propositions, on the one hand, and particular (I and O) propositions, on the other. The distinction is this. General propositions do not assert the existence of anything, while particular ones do.

Take an A proposition, "All Platonic ideas are eternal." According to the Venn analysis, this proposition asserts only that:

If there is a Platonic idea, then it is eternal.

It does *not*, however, assert that "There are Platonic ideas." This interpretation of general propositions is rather different from that most often used in daily discourse. For in ordinary conversation, when we assert a universal proposition, such as "All Poles are patriotic," we usually assert it together with the tacit assumption that there *are* such things as we are talking about. That is, when we say, "All Poles are patriotic," we assume "Of course, there are Poles." But according to the Venn analysis, an A or E proposition makes no assertion of the existence of whatever it may be talking about.

Even in ordinary language we sometimes use the non-existential interpretation of general propositions, although instances of this usage are rather limited. Consider the sign:

> All trespassers on this property are subject to prosecution.

The sentence painted on the signboard may very well be true, even though there may turn out to be no trespassers on the property. For, though the sign may be posted for a year, the class of "trespassers on this property" need not necessarily have any members. Similarly, the captain's order:

> No seasick men are excused from duty.

does not assert that there are seasick men. What these two notices *do* assert is (1) If there *is* a trespasser, then he is subject to prosecution, and (2) if there *is* a seasick man, he is not excused from duty.

On the other hand, particular and singular propositions, when analyzed by the Venn method, *do* assert the existence of what they are talking about. "Some tobaccos contain perique" does not assert that if there are some tobaccos, they contain perique, but rather that there is at least one member of the class "tobacco which contains perique." Similarly, when I state that some leprechauns do not wear green hats, I do not mean to say that if there are such things as leprechauns, then they do not wear green hats. I mean that there is at least one leprechaun and he does not wear a green hat.

We can see that the Venn diagram of the proposition "All angels have wings." does not show any area where *there are angels*. What the diagram does show is an area "angels-without-wings" ($a\overline{w}$) which does not have any existing members. In other words, the diagram shows only that *if* there is an angel, then it has wings. However, the Venn

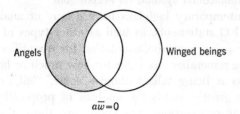

$a\overline{w}=0$

circles of the particular propositions *do* show the existence of what the proposition is talking about. The diagram of "Some Russians are chess players" shows by its 'x' that there is at least one Russian chess player.

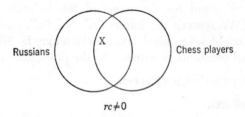

$rc\neq0$

In sum, the Venn diagrams illustrate and support analysis of the classical A, E, I, and O propositions according to the following formulae (null forms):

A. All beavers are brothers. $a\overline{b} = 0$ (There are no beavers who are not brothers.)

E. No delinquent boys are violinists. $ab = 0$ (Delinquent boys that are violinists form a class of no members.)

I. Some kings are stamp collectors. $ab \neq 0$ (Kings who are stamp collectors do not form a class without members; there is at least one king who is a stamp collector.)

O. Some wallabies are not certified public accountants. $a\overline{b} \neq 0$ (Wallabies who are not CPAs do not form a class of no members; there is at least one wallaby who is not a CPA.)

Quantification Symbols for Propositions

Contemporary logicians have a way of analyzing A, E, I, and O statements, as well as other types of propositions, by using a symbolic notation for quantifiers. Quantifiers, we remember, are signs for how much or how many of a class is being talked about—"some," "all," etc.—and their use greatly assists the analysis of propositions.

Singular propositions, we know, are those the subject terms of which are proper names, such as "Davy Crockett," or terms so restricted as to apply to only one individual, such as "this ocelot." Such propositions may be put in very simple notation by letting the capital letters, such as *F, G, H,* stand for predicates, while small letters *a* through *w* stand for the name of the individual talked about. (We reserve the letters "x," "y," "z,". . . for individual variables, i.e., blank spaces which may be filled in by individual constants or names.) So the proposition:

Davy Crockett is a pioneer.

is symbolized:

Pd

and the proposition:

This leopard has a temper.

becomes in symbolic form:

Tl

Negative singular propositions are constructed simply by placing a negation sign (−) in front of the predicate symbol:

−*Um*   Mozart is not a used-car salesman.
−*Ta*   That aardvark is not to be trusted.

We should note that the examples immediately above are *propositions*. No variables appear in them, as in:

Fx
Something is a fox.

which is not a proposition, but a *propositional function* only. "*Fx*" contains the symbol "*x*," which is an individual variable. Suppose we replace the variable with a name, such as Reynard; we now no longer have a propositional function, but rather a full-fledged singular proposition:

Fr
Reynard is a fox.

Existential Quantifiers

Now consider the proposition:

Ghosts exist.

What kind of proposition is this? It is not a singular proposition, for its subject term is not a proper name or its equivalent. It is not a general proposition such as "All ghosts are cousins," for "exist" is not a predicate such as "cousins" or "blue." It is a simpler assertion, stating only that there is at least one thing which is a ghost, or:

There are ghosts.

Let us introduce the symbol "$(\exists x)$" to stand for "There is something which is . . ." This symbol is known as the *existential quantifier*. It tells us that the proposition in which it appears asserts the existence of something. So we write:

$(\exists x)\ Gx$

This is symbolization for the proposition "There is something which is a ghost," or "There are ghosts," or simply "Ghosts exist."

Suppose we want to symbolize the *negative* of the original proposition. That is:

Ghosts do not exist.

All we need do here is to use the symbolic form of the affirmative proposition, prefacing this with a negation sign

"—." We read the negation sign as "It is not the case that," or simply "not." So we now have:

$$-(\exists x)\ Gx$$

which we may read, "It is not the case that there is something which is a ghost." More simply, "There are no ghosts," or "Ghosts do not exist." Note that the negation sign here means the denial of the *entire* expression "$(\exists x)\ Gx$."

Now let us write the symbolic notations for the propositions:

> There are kings.
> There are stamp collectors.

Remembering that F, G, etc., stand for predicates, we may write:

$(\exists x)\ Fx$	There is something which is a king.	(There are kings.)
$(\exists x)\ Gx$	There is something which is a stamp collector.[1]	(There are stamp collectors.)

Now suppose we want to symbolize the classical *particular affirmative* or I proposition:

> Some kings are stamp collectors.

We conjoin the two propositional functions Fx and Gx by means of the sign "$\cdot$," and precede the newly formed propositional function $(Fx \cdot Gx)$ by the existential quantifier:

$$(\exists x)(Fx \cdot Gx)$$

That is, there is something which is *both* a king and a stamp collector. Of course, this notation will do for *any* particular affirmative or I proposition:

> Some butterflies are blue.
> $(\exists x)(Fx \cdot Gx)$

That is, there is something which is both a butterfly and blue.

[1] From this point on we use as predicate symbols the letters F and G only. But the reader may, if he finds it helpful, continue to use the actual first letters of the terms: K for "king," S for "stamp collector," etc.

From the notational material we have at hand, we can easily construct the symbolic expression for the *universal negative* or E proposition.

No butterflies are blue.
$-(\exists x)(Fx \cdot Gx)$

That is, it is not the case that there is something which is a butterfly and blue. Now suppose we want to symbolize the *particular negative* or O proposition:

Some archangels are not messengers.
$(\exists x)(Fx \cdot -Gx)$

That is, there is something which is an archangel and which is *not* a messenger. Now, by placing a negative sign in front of the entire expression, we get the *universal affirmative* or A form:

All archangels are messengers.
$-(\exists x)(Fx \cdot -Gx)$

Summarizing, here are the forms of the A, E, I, and O propositions set forth using the existential quantification symbol $(\exists x)$:

A. *All grampuses breathe noisily.* $-(\exists x)(Fx \cdot -Gx)$
It is not the case that there is a grampus that doesn't breathe noisily.

E. *No oysters are ballet dancers.* $-(\exists x)(Fx \cdot Gx)$
It is not the case that there is an oyster that is a ballet dancer.

I. *Some dinosaurs blush easily.* $(\exists x)(Fx \cdot Gx)$
There is at least one dinosaur that blushes easily.

O. *Some gnus do not read the Bible.* $(\exists x)(Fx \cdot -Gx)$
There is at least one gnu that does not read the Bible.

Universal Quantifiers

Suppose we want to symbolize the forms of the traditional four propositions using, instead of the existential quantifier, the *universal* quantifier, which is written "(x)."

This symbol we read "for all x," or "everything is such that . . ." It tells us that the proposition in which it appears is general or universal. Suppose we are talking to a materialist. If his belief, "Everything is matter," is true, then each thing is material, no matter what that thing may be, a dog, a star, or a mind. Hence the proposition:

> Everything is matter.

has the form: $(x)\ Fx$

that is,

> Whatever x may be, x is matter.

or

> For all x, x is matter.

Using the universal quantifier (x), the letter symbols F, G, etc., to stand as before for predicates, and one additional symbol—the implication sign "$\supset$"—to stand for "implies" or "if . . . then . . ." we obtain the following forms:

A. *All waltzing mice are dizzy.* $(x)(Fx \supset Gx)$
   For all x, if x is F, then x is G.
   For all x if x is a waltzing
   mouse, then x is dizzy.

E. *No Englishmen are herbivorous.* $(x)(Fx \supset -Gx)$
   For all x, if x is F, x is not G.
   For all x, if x is an Englishman,
   x is not herbivorous.

I. *Some marsupials are existentialists.* $-(x)(Fx \supset -Gx)$
   It is not the case that for all x,
   if x is F, x is not G.
   It is not the case that for all x,
   if x is a marsupial, x is not an
   existentialist.

O. *Some barons are not robbers.* $-(x)(Fx \supset Gx)$
   It is not the case that for all x,
   if x is F, x is G.
   It is not the case that for all x,
   if x is a baron, x is a robber.

Finally, let us make up a table, using the universal quantifier "(x)" for the forms of the *general* (A and E) propositions, and the particular or existential quantifier "$(\exists x)$" for the forms of the particular propositions (I and O). In this way, the existential import of the I and O propositions will be shown in contrast to the A and E, which do not assert the existence of members of their subject classes:

A. *All basilisks glare.*
   For all x, if x is
   a basilisk, then x glares. $(x)(Fx \supset Gx)$

E. *No unicorns eat oats.*
   For all x, if x is
   a unicorn, x does not eat oats. $(x)(Fx \supset -Gx)$

I. *Some naiads are sorority sisters.*
   There is at least one x such that
   x is a naiad and a sorority sister. $(\exists x)(Fx \cdot Gx)$

O. *Some dragons do not breathe fire.*
   There is at least one x such that
   x is a dragon and does not breathe
   fire. $(\exists x)(Fx \cdot -Gx)$

QUESTIONS AND EXERCISES

1. Which of the following are propositions? Of those that are propositions, which are simple and which are compound?
   1. Ford Madox Ford is an English novelist.
   2. O past! O happy life! O songs of joy!
   3. Pardon me, are you Miss Beaver?
   4. Either that bartender is insolent or ignorant.
   5. If you put a penny in the slot, gum will come out.
   6. Somewhere I'll find you.
   7. Heaven is my destination and my postal address is Kalamazoo, Michigan.
   8. For all lost lovers let us truly pray this soft May morning.
   9. Thou art a philosopher. Speak to it, Horatio.
   10. Niobium has a low lattice-heat capacity.

2. Which of the following propositions explicitly state a relation of class inclusion or exclusion between subject and predicate terms.

1. She's a grand old girl.
2. Internal relations are more important than external relations.
3. The USSR controls the heartland of Asia.
4. Olive took me for a ride in her motorboat.
5. Sky waves are not as long as ground waves.
6. The pen of my aunt is in the pocket of my grandmother.
7. Itching powder is a mischievous invention.
8. Blood is thicker than water.
9. Pat's young friends are not respectable persons.
10. Post-office clerks are federal employees.

3. To which of the six standard propositions (A, E, I, O, singular affirmative, singular negative) are the following propositions most closely related? If necessary, translate them into the appropriate forms. Draw Euler or Venn diagrams for each, if possible.
   1. None of the wounded are missing.
   2. Every cat in this house has two tails.
   3. Logic is an utterly useless subject.
   4. Mesons are not visible particles.
   5. An Old Guard does not surrender.
   6. Everybody is not going to be placed in the job for which he is best qualified.
   7. At least one person here is an extortioner.
   8. The bluebird is a sign of happiness.
   9. Economists are extremely dismal people.
   10. Girls don't want long engagements.
   11. Guatemalans love music.
   12. Most obis are made of costly silk.
   13. St. Patrick is not a Frenchman.
   14. Some women are not coöperative.
   15. Several Presidents chew tobacco.

4. Invent Euler-type diagrams for the following propositions.
   1. Some lungfish are not soggy.
   2. The Finns are not Scandinavians.
   3. The *Suvorov* was Rozhdestvenski's flagship at Tsushima.
   4. Willis Lamb won the Nobel Prize for physics.
   5. Not every Cornell faculty member is a cannibal.
   6. Peter Warlock wrote the carol "Corpus Christi."
   7. That man's mother is not my aunt.
   8. Every dead soldier is a hero.
   9. Few wallabies are good jumpers.

    10. The absent are always wrong.

    11. Molly Bloom is not the heroine of *Finnegans Wake*.

    12. Only followers of Dada are admitted without a ticket.

    13. Achilles is a shade.

    14. Cherubim are not owners of dry-cleaning establishments.

    15. Not one rhinoceros is disloyal.

5. Invent Venn diagrams for the following propositions.

    1. The meek shall inherit the earth.

    2. One honey bear has volunteered.

    3. Every telling has a tailing.

    4. Whenever a baby carriage is inhabited, that is a potentially dangerous situation.

    5. A few stragglers are absent without leave.

    6. At least one music critic does not have a red-haired wife.

    7. Some members of the library committee are members of the house committee.

    8. No alligator devours his own nose.

    9. Certain German romantics were precursors of national socialism.

    10. Sherifs are descendants of Mohammed.

    11. Many European bisons are not college graduates.

    12. A happy man is he who dies for his country.

    13. Crocuses are hardy plants.

    14. Whoever degrades another degrades me.

    15. Nations outside the Security Council are not members of the United Nations.

6. Explain, using your own illustrations, what it means to say that particular propositions have existential import, while general ones do not. Show by means of Venn diagrams the essential difference between these two types of propositions.

7. Consider the following objections to the doctrine of existential import of particular propositions. Are they refutable?

    1. "Particular propositions cannot assert existence. For I can say, 'Some mermaids have long tails.' Yet everybody knows there are no such things as mermaids."

    2. "If the doctrine of existential import of particular and singular propositions is true, then I can prove the existence of God simply by saying 'God exists.'"

8. Put the following propositions into one of the four forms:

$$1.\ a\bar{b} = 0$$
$$2.\ ab = 0$$
$$3.\ ab \neq 0$$
$$4.\ a\bar{b} \neq 0$$

But instead of using a and b for the subject and predicate terms, use the initial letter of one of the words composing the terms. Thus, "Unicorns are fabulous monsters" would be symbolized by $u\bar{f} = 0$

1. Some bus drivers are not aesthetes.
2. Many Trojans are eaters of bread.
3. Only fools are insulters of aardvarks.
4. The Blemys have no shoulders.
5. A number of motion-picture actresses read Tolstoy.
6. Bokhara rugs are precious objects.
7. The duck-billed platypus is an oviparous mammal.
8. A few babies subscribe to *The Atlantic Monthly*.
9. Some rare earths are not radioactive substances.
10. Not a single nurse is among the survivors.
11. Every Valkyrie rides a horse.
12. Among those who have confused ideas are turnips.
13. Most of Henry Green's admirers are not good judges of literature.
14. Some members of the present cabinet are not Tories.
15. At least one ophthalmologist belongs to the County Medical Society.

9. Put the propositions in Question 8 above into forms using particular quantifiers. Follow the same procedure for notation of subject and predicate terms.

10. Put the propositions in Question 8 into forms using universal quantifiers.

3

Inferences from Simple Propositions

The Distribution of Terms

In the classical analysis of propositions, there is a very simple analysis of quantification called the distribution of terms. We know that if we break our propositions down into two terms and a copula, the *subject term* is that which the proposition is talking about, and the *predicate term* is that which is asserted about the subject. In these class-membership propositions, the *copula* is that part of the verb "to be" which links subject and predicate terms. Thus in the proposition

All tenors are short men

the subject term is "tenors" and the predicate term is "short men." The copula is "are." Now in this proposition, the subject term "tenors" is *distributed*. This means that *all* of the subject class is referred to. But in the proposition

Some Tibetans are devil worshipers

the subject term "Tibetans" is undistributed because only *some* of that class is referred to.

Let us look once more at each of the four classical propositions (A, E, I, O) in order to decide whether the subject and predicate of each proposition is distributed or not. (If you draw circle diagrams, it will help to make the distribution of each term clear.)

A. All kangaroos are introverts.
E. No poets are actuaries.
I. Some ballet dancers are temperamental.
O. Some dreams are not wish fulfillments.

The distribution of the subject term in each proposition gives little trouble. In the A proposition, the subject term is "kangaroos." It is obviously distributed, because the prefixed quantifying word "all" tells us that the entire class of kangaroos is being talked about. In the E proposition, the subject is also distributed, even though the word prefixed to the sentence is negative ("no"). For the E proposition asserts that it is *untrue* of *all* poets that they are actuaries. The subject terms of the I and O propositions carry an explicit "some" quantifier. Hence we know that only *part* of the classes "ballet dancers" and "dreams" is referred to. Hence we say that the subject terms of the I and O propositions are *undistributed*.

The distribution of the predicate terms of the four propositions is less obvious, since in ordinary language predicate terms do not carry quantifying words like "some" or "all" before them. When we say, "All kangaroos are introverts," we do not assert that kangaroos exhaust the class of introverts. Nor when we say, "All Hawaiians are good swimmers," do we mean that Hawaiians are *all* of the good swimmers. From the information given to us by the proposition at hand, we can go no further than to assert that "All kangaroos are *some* of the introverts," although this does not mean that we know anything at all about the introverts that are *not* kangaroos, if indeed there are any. We simply conclude that the predicate term "bachelors" is *undistributed*. This holds for A propositions generally.

The predicate term of an E proposition is distributed for the same reason that the subject is distributed. Just as it is untrue of *all* poets that they are actuaries, so also it is untrue of *all* actuaries that they are poets. In E propositions, both subject and predicate classes are excluded from one another in their entirety. Thus the predicate "actuaries" is *distributed,* and this holds for the predicates of all E propositions.

The predicate terms of particular affirmative (I) propositions are *undistributed*. The assertion that some ballet dancers are temperamental should not be taken as intending that some ballet dancers are *all* of those who possess this property. From the information given to us by the proposition, we do not know whether this is so. We may safely assume only that the "some ballet dancers" talked about may not exhaust the class of those who are temperamental. Hence the predicate "temperamental" is *undistributed* and such is the case with I propositions generally.

The predicate terms of particular negative (O) propositions are *distributed*. In the given example, "Some dreams are not wish fulfillments," the predicate term is, of course, "wish fulfillments." Is the entire class of wish fulfillments excluded from the "some dreams" we are talking about? A little reflection, together with a glance at a scratch-pad Euler or Venn diagram of the proposition, will disclose that such is the case. When we say "Some dreams are not wish fulfillments," we must admit that the "some dreams" referred to are separated from the *entire class* of wish fulfillments. Since the whole of the predicate class is excluded from the "dreams" meant, we must conclude that the predicate term "wish fulfillments" is *distributed* and that this holds for any and all O propositions.

We may now draw up a table showing the distribution of subject and predicate terms for A, E, I, and O propositions:

Subject Term	Predicate Term
A. distributed	undistributed
E. distributed	distributed
I. undistributed	undistributed
O. undistributed	distributed

Simple Propositional Inferences: Conversion

By making certain formal alterations in the structure of two-term propositions, we can derive new propositions from the originals. Such simple inferences are known in classical logic as "immediate inferences." In *conversion,* we simply transpose the subject and predicate terms of a proposition in such a way that the second proposition is validly inferable from the first. The proposition to be converted (that is, the original proposition) is called the *convertend*. The result is called the *converse*.

Convertend	Converse
A. All great men are bad writers.	Some bad writers are great men.
E. No dodoes are great auks.	No great auks are dodoes.
I. Some blondes have blue eyes.	Some that have blue eyes are blondes.

Particular negative (O) propositions cannot be converted. If they appear to convert successfully, the chances are that we have done more than transpose the subject and predicate term of the proposition. For example, in the case of the proposition "Some carbon compounds are not organic," the proposition "Some inorganic things are carbon compounds" is *not* the converse. Rather, as we shall see, the second is the "partial contraposition" of the first.

We might think that in the case of O propositions, the converse of "Some mammals are not carnivores" is "Some carnivores are not mammals." But a little reflection will show that the second is not validly inferrible from the first. Suppose someone says "Some music is not opera." It does not follow that therefore "Some opera is not music." The difficulty here, technically stated, is that we cannot derive a distributed term in the converse from an undistributed term in the convertend. To make a rule of it: *From a proposition in which a term is undistributed, we cannot infer a proposition in which that term is distributed.* In other words, one cannot formally infer that what holds for "some" must on that account also hold for "all."

The subject terms of E and I propositions, when those propositions have been converted, show the same distribution value as the subject terms of their respective convertends. But in the case of A propositions, the subject term of the converse is *undistributed* while the subject term of the convertend is *distributed*. For the predicate of the A proposition is undistributed, and in the converse (where this term becomes the subject) must remain undistributed.

Correct: All beagles are good hunters.
             Therefore, some good hunters are beagles.
Incorrect: All hotel musicians are union members.
             Therefore, all union members are hotel musi-
             cians.

Traditional nomenclature assigns the label "simple conversion" to conversions of the E and I type. In the case
of A propositions—where the distribution of the subject
of the converse always differs from the distribution of the
subject of the convertend—conversions are known as
"Conversions *per accidens*."

Obversion

To obtain the obverse of a proposition, two things
must be done: (1) Change the *quality* of the original
proposition (the obvertend); that is, if the original proposition is negative, change it to affirmative, or vice versa.
(2) *Negate* the predicate term of the obvertend by at-
taching the prefix "non-" to it. To negate "organic," make
it "nonorganic" or "inorganic"; to negate "polite" change
it to "nonpolite" or "impolite," etc. We should never try
to handle two loose or "floating" negatives in one proposition. Statements like "No cats are not mouse hunters"
are nonsense in classical logic.

	Obvertend	*Obverse*
A.	All poets are practical.	No poets are nonpractical.
E.	No idiots are responsible.	All idiots are nonresponsible.
I.	Some teachers are wise.	Some teachers are not nonwise.
O.	Some phosphorus is not in-flammable.	Some phosphorus is nonin-flammable.

Partial Contraposition

Partial contrapositions of propositions may be obtained by (1) getting the *obverse* of the original proposition, then (2) obtaining the *converse* of the result. In
other words, a partial contraposition is the converse of an
obverse.

Original	*Partial Contraposition*
A.	All airplane mechanics are employed.	No unemployed are airplane mechanics.
E.	No cold-blooded animals are mammals.	Some nonmammals are cold-blooded animals.
I.	. . . .	. . . .
O.	Some New Zealanders are not Polynesians.	Some non-Polynesians are New Zealanders.

We note that I propositions cannot be subjected to partial contraposition, since this process requires obverting the I proposition, and thus obtaining an O. But O propositions cannot be converted.

Full Contraposition

To obtain the full contraposition of a proposition, we *obvert the partial contraposition* of that proposition.

Original	*Full Contraposition*
A.	All pin boys are Phi Beta Kappas.	All non-Phi Beta Kappas are non-pin boys
E.	No calypso singers are Bostonians.	Some non-Bostonians are not non-calypso singers.
I.	. . . .	. . . .
O.	Some butterflies are not blue.	Some nonblue things are not nonbutterflies.

As far as the results are concerned, there is no difference between the full contraposition of an E and that of an O proposition.

Obverting the Converse

If we reverse the order of the steps involved in partial contraposition, we obtain an obverted converse. That is, we first *convert* the original proposition, then we *obvert* it.

Original	*Obverted Converse*
A.	All galagos are pessimists.	Some pessimists are not non-galagos.
E.	No members of the library committee are members of the social committee.	All members of the social committee are nonmembers of the library committee.
I.	Some artists are bohemians.	Some bohemians are not non-artists.

Are Inferences from General to Particular Valid?

We know that it is formally invalid to infer a general proposition from a particular. If I am informed that "Some arthritis is curable," I cannot conclude that therefore "All arthritis is curable." But what about the other way around? Given the proposition "All members of Locust Valley are Republicans," it seems to follow (by conversion *per accidens*) that "Some Republicans are residents of Locust Valley." But if the modern doctrine of the nonexistential import of general propositions holds (see p. 19), then it would appear that particular propositions *cannot* be inferred from general ones. For, according to this doctrine, general propositions do not assert the existence of what they are talking about, while particular ones do. Such an analysis appears to compromise the validity of many of the simple propositional inferences illustrated above, as well as the correctness of a number of syllogistic inferences we have yet to examine. The difficulty may be by-passed, however, if we assume in such exercises (as did the classical logicians) *that every class dealt with has at least one member.*

THE SQUARE OF OPPOSITION

The square of opposition is a device of classical logic which graphically represents certain relations between propositions. Some of these propositions are logically "opposed," others not. Here are the names of these relations between propositions, together with illustrations:

Contradictories

Two propositions are contradictory if both cannot be true together nor both false together. In other words, of two contradictory propositions, one must be true and the other false. Of the four basic types, A and O are contradictory; so are E and I.

All Siamese cats have kinked tails.
Some Siamese do not have kinked tails.

No Englishmen fail to do their duty.
Some Englishmen fail to do their duty.

Contraries

Two propositions are contrary if both cannot simultaneously be true, but both can be false. A and E are contraries.

All Easter bunnies melt easily.
No Easter bunnies melt easily.

Subcontraries

Two propositions are subcontraries if they can both simultaneously be true, but not both false. I and O are subcontraries.

Some Papuans wear nose bones.
Some Papuans do not wear nose bones.

Subaltern and Superaltern

A subaltern is the particular counterpart of a general proposition. I is the subaltern of A, and O is the subaltern of E.

Some babies resemble chimpanzees.   *is the subaltern of*
All babies resemble chimpanzees.

Some pobbles do not have toes.   *is the subaltern of*
No pobbles have toes.

A superaltern is the general or universal counterpart of a particular proposition. A is the superaltern of I, and E is the superaltern of O.

All bicycle riders are subversive.   *is the superaltern of*
Some bicycle riders are subversive.

No oboe players are bald.   *is the superaltern of*
Some oboe players are not bald.

If any superaltern is true, its subaltern is also true. But if any subaltern is true, its superaltern may or may not be true. If any subaltern is false, its superaltern is also false. But if any superaltern is false, its subaltern may or may not be false.

Equivalents

Two propositions are equivalent if they are true together and false together. That is, when p is true, q is true, and when q is true, p is true; also when p is false, q is false, and when q is false, p is false.

> All women are coöperative.
> No women are uncoöperative.

Obverses, for example, bear the relation of equivalence to their respective originals. (Modern logic distinguishes between certain important kinds of equivalence; this we shall see in Chapter 6.)

Independents

Two propositions are independent of one another when the truth or falsity of one is unrelated to the truth or falsity of the other:

> The United States ambassador has just landed at Geneva.
> A *modinha* is a sentimental Brazilian song.

The Square Constructed: Truth Tables

The relationships above may be quickly appreciated when the opposed propositions are in position on the square.

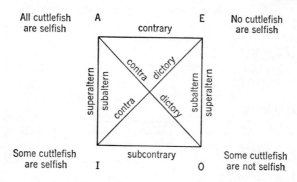

On the basis of this square, we can construct a simple *truth table*. For example, if A ("All cuttlefish are selfish") is true, then its contradictory ("Some cuttlefish are not selfish") must be false. If "Some mice have tails" is true, then its superaltern "All mice have tails" and its sub-contrary "Some mice do not have tails" are *undetermined* or doubtful. That is, we cannot tell whether such propositions are true or false, since both their truth and falsity are consistent with the truth of the given proposition. But if, for example, "Some mice have tails" is assumed to be *false*, its superaltern, "All mice have tails," will also be false; but its subcontrary, "Some mice do not have tails," will be true.

We should see why the truth of an I proposition does not in and of itself imply the truth of its subcontrary. If "Some S is P" is true, it does not follow that "Some S is not P" is also true. If I know that some cases of arthritis are curable, and nothing beyond this, then it may or may not be the case that some cases of arthritis are incurable. If I am informed that "Some Bryn Mawr girls are pretty," I can no more infer from that information that "Some Bryn Mawr girls are not pretty" than I can from a man's statement that he has four legitimate children conclude that therefore he has a certain number of illegitimate ones.

Setting out the tables, using T for true, F for false, and U for undetermined, we have:

	A	E	I	O
If A is true	T	F	T	F
If E is true				
If I is true	U	F	T	U
If O is true				
If A is false				
If E is false				
If I is false				
If O is false				

As an exercise, the reader may fill in the rest of the spaces himself.

What about the contradictories of *singular* statements? Pairs of singular statements cannot be contraries, but they can certainly contradict one another. The contradictory of "Pluto is a planet" is "Pluto is not a planet," or "It is not the case that Pluto is a planet." The contradictory of "Pope Innocent did not hate King Francis" is "It is not the case that Pope Innocent did not hate King Francis," or, more simply, "Pope Innocent hated King Francis."

The Contradictories in Modern Symbolic Notation

Let us recall for a moment our analysis of classical propositions by means of quantification symbols (pp. 22 *et seq.*). Suppose we express the four basic propositional forms in terms of the existential quantifier $(\exists x)$, placing them in their appropriate positions on the square of opposition. We can see that the contradictory of $(\exists x) (Fx \cdot Gx)$

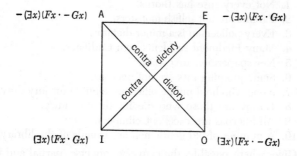

$-(\exists x)(Fx \cdot -Gx)$ A .... E $-(\exists x)(Fx \cdot Gx)$

contra dictory

contra dictory

$(\exists x)(Fx \cdot Gx)$ I .... O $(\exists x)(Fx \cdot -Gx)$

("There is an x which is both F and G") is simply the negation of that expression $-(\exists x) (Fx \cdot Gx)$ ("It is not the case that there is an x which is both F and G"). That is, the E proposition is the contradictory of the I. Similarly, the contradictory of $(\exists x) (Fx \cdot -Gx)$ ("There is an x which is F and not G") *is* $-(\exists x) (Fx \cdot -Gx)$ ("It is not the case that there is an x which is F and not G"). In other words, the A proposition is the contradictory of the O.

If we choose to express the four propositional forms in the

symbolic notation associated with the Venn diagrams
(p. 17), then we can see that $ab \neq 0$ (particular affirmative I) is simply the negation or contradictory of $ab = 0$
(universal negative E). in the same way, $a\bar{b} \neq 0$ (particular
negative O) is the negation or contradictory of $a\bar{b} = 0$.

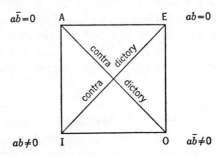

QUESTIONS AND EXERCISES

1. Explain why the subject and predicate terms in each of the
   following propositions are distributed or undistributed. Use
   circle diagrams in your explanation.
   1. Not every rose has thorns.
   2. Parents are not selfish monsters.
   3. Every policeman is a minor dictator.
   4. Many Piedmont residents own Cadillacs.
   5. Newspapermen are cynics.
   6. Some jumping rats are not nervous.
   7. None who hold public office are eligible for jury duty.
   8. Happy are those who die for their country.
   9. All Sherpas are excellent climbers.
   10. A number of old gentlemen are friends of the library.

2. Give, where possible, the converse, obverse, partial and full
   contraposition, and obverted converse of each of the following:
   1. All pin boys are Phi Beta Kappas.
   2. No bishops are queens.
   3. Some quarterbacks are captains.
   4. Some shortstops are not philosophers.
   5. Every die is a cube.
   6. Not one spade is red.
   7. Several champions are professionals.
   8. A few goalies are not ambidexterous.

9. Pole vaulters are not milers.

10. All wrestlers are followers of Stanislavski.

3. Given "No basenjis are watchdogs," which of the following may validly be inferred, and which not? Explain, using circle diagrams in each case.

1. All nonwatchdogs are basenjis.

2. Some nonwatchdogs are not nonbasenjis.

3. Some watchdogs are nonbasenjis.

4. Some nonwatchdogs are not nonbasenjis.

5. No watchdogs are basenjis.

4. Given "All violinists are musicians," which of the following may validly be inferred, and which not? Explain, using circle diagrams in each case.

1. Some nonmusicians are nonviolinists.

2. Some musicians are not nonviolinists.

3. Some nonmusicians are not violinists.

4. Some nonviolinists are not musicians.

5. All musicians are nonviolinists.

5. A. I have propositions *p* and *q* such that:
   When *p* is true, *q* is false;
   when *p* is false, *q* is false.

   B. I have propositions *r* and *s* such that:
   When *r* is true, *s* is true;
   when *r* is false, *s* is false.

   C. I have propositions *t* and *u* such that:
   When *t* is true, *u* is undetermined;
   when *t* is false, *u* is undetermined.

   D. I have propositions *m* and *n* such that:
   When *m* is true, *n* is undetermined;
   when *m* is false, *n* is true.

   E. I have propositions *u* and *v* such that:
   When *u* is true, *v* is false;
   when *v* is true, *u* is false.

   What is the most appropriate name of the relationship between the propositions in each case?

6. Does "Some gibbons beat their babies" imply "Some gibbons do not beat their babies"? Explain carefully.

7. Give the most appropriate name to the relation between the propositions in the following pairs:

   (1) A. No grampuses use Kleenex.
   B. Some non-Kleenex users are not nongrampuses.

(2) A. I love you.
   B. You love me.

(3) A. All babies are illiterate.
   B. None that are literate are babies.

(4) A. Not an aardvark was stirring.
   B. At least one aardvark was stirring.

(5) A. Some nearsighted things are not non-Moslems.
   B. Some Moslems are nearsighted.

8. Give, where possible, the contradictory, contrary, subcontrary, subaltern, or superaltern of the following propositions:

1. All Javanese children are expert dancers.
2. Not every giraffe is amiable.
3. No well-born Arabs are guides.
4. Some American flowers are of Chinese origin.
5. U. S. Grant was a four-star general.
6. It is not the case that Marlowe wrote *Hamlet*.
7. Every planet moves in an elliptical orbit.
8. Some double-bass players pay extra fare.
9. All neuroses are rooted in childhood.
10. Gnus are not three-letter words.

9. Explain just why it is that if "All Malays chew betel" is false, "No Malays chew betel" is undetermined.

10. Which of the following inferences are valid? Explain in each case.

1. All merchant ships are commercial carriers; therefore all Greek merchant shippers are Greek commercial carriers.
2. All white eagles are white birds; therefore, all eagles are birds.
3. All the wives on this street are mothers; therefore, all unfaithful wives on this street are unfaithful mothers.

4

The Syllogism (I)

The syllogism is a form of deductive argument in which, granting the truth of two statements (called the premises), the truth of a third statement (the conclusion) necessarily follows. Syllogisms are classified as (1) *categorical* and (2) *conditional*. Categorical syllogisms are composed of three simple or noncompound propositions. Here is an example of a categorical syllogism:

All alkaloids are poisonous.
Strychnine is an alkaloid.

Therefore, strychnine is poisonous.

Conditional syllogisms fall into two subclasses: (1) *hypothetical* or implicative syllogisms ("if . . . then"); and (2) *alternative-disjunctive* or "either . . . or" syllogisms. Examples would be:

1. Hypothetical syllogism:

If the patient has fever, he is infected.
The patient has fever.

∴ He is infected.

2. Alternative-disjunctive syllogism:

Either Pat was joking or she really loved him.
Pat was not joking.

∴ She really loved him.

The larger part of the classical doctrine of the syllogism is devoted to the *categorical* syllogism. This we shall now examine.

Structure of the Categorical Syllogism

We may consider the following syllogism as typical:

All marsupials are vertebrates.
All wallabies are marsupials.
∴ All wallabies are vertebrates.

The first proposition is called the *major premise,* the second is called the *minor premise,* and the third is called the *conclusion.* The term which occurs once in the major premise and once in the conclusion is called the *major term.* The term which occurs once in the minor premise and once in the conclusion is called the *minor term.* The term which occurs once in the major premise and once in the minor premise (and *never* in the conclusion) is called the *middle term.* In the syllogism illustrated, the major term is "vertebrates," the minor term "wallabies," and the middle "marsupials."

Rules of the Categorical Syllogism

Some syllogisms are valid; others are not. The following rules are given by means of which we may determine the validity of categorical syllogisms:

1. *The syllogism must have three and only three terms.* The following syllogism violates this rule:

Cats like cream.
Kittens are pets.
∴ Kittens like cream.

It is clear in the syllogism above that there are four terms: (1) "cats," (2) "like cream," (3) "pets," (4) "kittens." Hence the syllogism commits "the fallacy of four terms." In certain syllogisms, the middle term is ambiguous or double-meaninged, thereby creating what is in effect the fallacy of four terms. Consider the following:

No nice girl swears.
Caroline, when called to the witness stand, swore.
∴ Caroline, when called to the witness stand, was not a nice girl.

Taken as an argument in which attention must be paid to the *meanings* of terms rather than as a purely formal inference pattern, the syllogism above would commit the fallacy of four terms. For the middle term "swear" is used in one sense in the major premise ("to use improper language") and in another sense in the minor premise ("to take a legal oath"), thereby, in effect, creating four terms.

2. *The syllogism must have three and only three propositions.* This is obvious, and requires no illustration.

3. *The middle term must be distributed once at least.* Consider the following syllogism:

> All Democrats are Americans.
> All Republicans are Americans.
> ∴ All Republicans are Democrats.

It is evident that simply because two subclasses happen to belong to one and the same class, it does not follow that they are identical with each other. Because ducks swim, and you do too, it does not follow that you are a duck. (It does not follow that you are *not* a duck, either.) The error in the syllogism above is known as "the fallacy of the undistributed middle term." Here is another example, with the undistributed middle marked:

> All Socialists *favor organization of the workers* (undis).
> All labor unionists *favor organization of the workers* (undis).
> ∴ All labor unionists are Socialists.

The middle term, "favor organization of the workers," is undistributed in each premise because it is the predicate term of an A proposition. (Review the topic of Distribution of Terms, p. 31.)

4. *If a term is distributed in the conclusion, it must also be distributed in its proper premise.*

Only two terms appear in the conclusion of a syllogism, the minor and major terms. Therefore, we have two and only two possible ways of violating this rule. (1) The major term may be distributed in the conclusion and undistributed in the major premise. This is known as the "illicit process of the major." Or (2) the minor term may be distributed in the conclusion and undistributed in the minor premise. This is known as the "illicit process of the minor."

Here is an example of the illicit major:

> All mathematicians are good-tempered.
> No poets are mathematicians.
> ──────────────────────────────
> ∴ No poets are good-tempered.

Here is another example, with the distribution marked:

> Pterodactyls are *prehistoric animals* (undis).
> Shetland ponies are not pterodactyls.
> ──────────────────────────────
> ∴ Shetland ponies are not *prehistoric animals* (dis).

In the syllogism above, the major term "prehistoric animals" is distributed in the conclusion (it is the predicate term of an E proposition), but it is undistributed in the major premise (for it is the predicate term of an A proposition). Hence, it is an illicit process of the major.

Here is an example of the illicit minor:

> Those who lack culture should take a humanities course.
> Many sophomores lack culture.
> ──────────────────────────────
> ∴ All sophomores should take a humanities course.

Here is another example of the fallacy of the illicit minor, with the distribution of the minor term marked:

> No birds are viviparous.
> All birds are *bipeds* (undis).
> ──────────────────────────────
> ∴ No *bipeds* (dis) are viviparous.

In the syllogism above, the minor term "bipeds" is distributed in the conclusion (subject term of an E proposition), but it is undistributed in the minor premise (predicate term of an A proposition). Hence, it is an illicit minor.

5. *From two negative premises, no conclusion can be drawn.* Given the two premises:

> No peat is anthracite.
> No bituminous coal is anthracite.

we cannot infer that:

> No bituminous coal is peat.

Because two classes are both excluded from one and the same third class, it does not follow that they have or have not anything to do with each other. Violation of this rule may be called the "fallacy of the two negative premises."

6. *From two particular premises, no conclusion can be drawn.* Here is an example of a violation of this rule:

> Some cocktails are too sweet.
> Some mixed drinks are cocktails.
> ∴ Some mixed drinks are too sweet.

We note that this syllogism also violates an earlier rule, since the middle term is twice undistributed. Thus, it commits the fallacy of the "undistributed middle" as well as that of the "two particular premises."

7. *If one premise is negative, the conclusion must be negative.* An example of a violation of this rule would be:

> No bats are viola players.
> All bats bite toes.
> ∴ Some that bite toes are viola players.

8. *If one premise is particular, the conclusion must be particular.* Here is an example of a violation of this rule:

> Bedlington terriers look like lambs.
> Some Bedlington terriers look like rats.
> ∴ All that look like rats look like lambs.

We can see that this syllogism also violates the rule which says that no term may be distributed in the conclusion which was not already distributed in its proper premise. In other words, an illicit minor is committed here as well as a violation of the present rule.

9. *From two affirmative premises, a negative conclusion cannot be drawn.* An example of a violation of this rule follows:

> All teddy-bears are bad-mannered.
> Those who are bad-mannered will be punished.
> ∴ Some who will be punished are not teddy-bears.

MOODS AND FIGURES OF THE CATEGORICAL SYLLOGISM

Mood

Every syllogism has three propositions, and each proposition may be either an A, E, I, or O proposition. The *mood* of a syllogism refers to the particular combination of propositions that make it up. For example, the following syllogism is in the mood AAA:

> All Scotsmen are thrifty.
> All gillies are Scotsmen.
> ∴ All gillies are thrifty.

That is, the major premise of the syllogism is an A proposition, so too is its minor, and its conclusion. A syllogism in the mood EAO would be one in which the major premise is an E proposition, the minor an A, and the conclusion an O.

How many possible moods are there? The question whether or not they are valid being set aside for the moment, we can see that there are 64 possible moods of the categorical syllogism. They are:

AAA	AIA	EAA	EIA	IAA	IIA	OAA	OIA
AAE	AIE	EAE	EIE	IAE	IIE	OAE	OIE
AAI	AII	EAI	EII	IAI	III	OAI	OIJ
AAO	AIO	EAO	EIO	IAO	IIO	OAO	OIO
AEA	AOA	EEA	EOA	IEA	IOA	OEA	OOA
AEE	AOE	EEE	EOE	IEE	IOE	OEE	OOE
AEI	AOI	EEI	EOI	IEI	IOI	OEI	OOI
AEO	AOO	EEO	EOO	IEO	IOO	OEO	OOO

Now suppose we test these 64 possible moods according to the rules of the syllogism. On simple inspection, we find that we dismiss many of these syllogisms as invalid, without going to the bother of constructing them. For example, all the OO's may be dismissed as invalid, because of the rule forbidding two negative premises as well as the rule against two particular premises. All the EE's go out, because of the rule concerning two negative premises. The II's the IO's, and the OI's are eliminated by the rule concerning two particular premises. AAO is scratched by virtue of Rule 9; AIE by Rule 8, and so forth.

After completing this process of elimination by simple inspection, we find that we have twelve moods remaining which we may tentatively take to be valid. They are:

AAA	EAE	IAI	OAO
AAI	EAO	IEO	
AEE	EIO		
AEO			
AII			
AOO			

But we cannot yet consider these moods valid until we have constructed each syllogism in each of the four *figures*.

Figure

The figure of a syllogism refers to the *position of the middle term* in the premises of the syllogism. If we look at the following four syllogisms, we notice they are all in the same *mood* (AAA), but that the position of the middle term is different in each case.

1. All *orchids* are parasites.
   All cattleyas are *orchids*.
   ∴ All cattleyas are parasites.

2. All koalas are *good*.
   All little girls are *good*.
   ∴ All little girls are koalas.

3. All *oboists* are bald.
   All *oboists* play chess.
   ∴ All who play chess are bald.

4. All guppies *eat their children*.
   All *who eat their children* are rude.
   ∴ All who are rude are guppies.

Now, of the syllogisms above, only the first is valid. The second commits the fallacy of the undistributed middle term, while three and four are guilty of the illicit process of the minor. That is, AAA is *valid only in the first figure;* it is invalid in the other three.

The following schema shows the position of the terms in each of the four figures. If we let X stand for the major term, Y for the middle term, and Z for the minor term, the figures are as follows:

	1st Figure	2nd Figure	3rd Figure	4th Figure
	YX	XY	YX	XY
	ZY	ZY	YZ	YZ
	ZX	ZX	ZX	ZX

By convention, the order of terms in the conclusion of a syllogism is always minor-major (ZX).

Now if we take each of the 12 moods we were left with above and construct them in each of these four figures, we shall discover that of the 48 resulting syllogisms, only 24 will pass the test of the rules. Here they are:

1st Figure	2nd Figure	3rd Figure	4th Figure
AAA	EAE	**AAI**	EIO
EAE	AEE	AII	**AAI**
AII	EIO	IAI	AEE
EIO	AOO	EIO	**EAO**
		EAO	IAI
(AAI)	(EAO)	OAO	
(EAO)	(AEO)		(AEO)

Weakened Conclusions and Strengthened Premises

The five syllogisms in parentheses above are valid according to the rules of the syllogism. But they have "weakened conclusions." That is, they draw *particular* (I and O) conclusions when, from the premises, they might just as well have drawn *general* conclusions (A or E). For example, suppose we take AAI (first figure):

> All Frenchmen respect poets.
> All residents of Toulon are Frenchmen.
> ∴ Some residents of Toulon respect poets.

It is clear that, from the premises above, we could validly have drawn the conclusion "*All* residents of Toulon respect poets." That is why AAI in the first figure and the other four syllogisms in parentheses are known as syllogisms with weakened conclusions.

The four syllogisms in the table above in bold face (as well as all five syllogisms with weakened conclusions) are syllogisms with *strengthened premises*. All have two general or universal premises and a particular conclusion. Now these syllogisms could draw the same conclusion even if one of their premises were reduced from general to particular. For example, consider EAO, fourth figure:

> No crocodiles are voters.
> All voters are literate.
> _____
> ∴ Some who are literate are not crocodiles.

It is obvious that this same conclusion could be reached validly if for the minor premise should be substituted its particular form or subaltern—"Some voters are literate."

We shall see that syllogisms with strengthened premises or weakened conclusions fail to pass certain relatively modern tests we are about to examine. The reason is that in these interesting syllogisms, a particular conclusion is inferred from two general premises. If particular propositions are taken (as in the Venn analysis) to assert existence, and general propositions as not asserting existence (see p. 19), then universal and particular propositions are of radically different import. But if this is so, particular conclusions cannot be inferred from general premises. However, we know that classical logicians interpreted both general and particular propositions existentially. Hence syllogisms with strengthened premises and weakened conclusions are valid by traditional rules.

Code Names for Valid Syllogisms

Traditional logic preserves certain code names which medieval logicians invented to help students learn the valid syllogisms in each mood and figure, and to assist in the performance of certain syllogistic exercises. These code names are quaint, but (as we shall see) oddly useful. The code name of the syllogism in AAA, first figure, is BARBARA; that of EAE, second figure CESARE. The vowels of the code names stand for the *mood* of the syllogism. Certain of the consonants in the code names are also significant. Here is a complete list of the code names:

1st Figure	*2nd Figure*	*3rd Figure*	*4th Figure*
BARBARA	CESARE	DARAPTI	FRESISON
CELARENT	CAMESTRES	DATISI	BRAMANTIP
DARII	FESTINO	DISAMIS	CAMENES
FERIO	BAROCO	FERISON	FESAPO
		FELAPTON	DIMARIS
(AAI)	(EAO)	BOCARDO	
(EAO)	(AEO)		(AEO)

Syllogisms with weakened conclusion have no code names, and are listed in parentheses. The syllogisms with strengthened premises, however, have code names; they are (in the third figure) DARAPTI and FELAPTON, and (in the fourth figure) BRAMANTIP and FESAPO.

A Second Test of Validity: Venn Diagrams

The syllogism may be treated as a device to show the relations between three classes. Hence we can diagram syllogisms with three intersecting Venn circles, each of which represents a class. One circle stands for the class designated by the major term; another for that of the minor; the third for the class of the middle term. Let us take a syllogism in BARBARA (AAA, first figure):

> All whales are introverts.
> <u>All grampuses are whales.</u>
> ∴ All grampuses are introverts.

If we diagram this syllogism with three Venn circles, we see that places are reserved for a number of subclasses produced by the intersection of the three class circles:

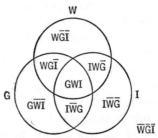

The center area GWI will accommodate those that are whales, introverts, and grampuses. The area at the extreme lower left G$\overline{\text{W}}\overline{\text{I}}$ is available for grampuses, nonwhales, and nonintroverts. The area at the extreme lower right $I\overline{W}\overline{G}$ is reserved for introverts who are neither grampuses nor whales, and so forth.

Now let us take the major premise:

All whales are introverts.

From our earlier study of the Venn diagrams, we know that the form of this proposition may be expressed:

$$w\bar{\imath} = 0$$

That is, whales that are not introverts form a class of no members; there are no nonintroverted whales. Accordingly, let us shade in that area of the "whale" circle *outside* the "introvert" circle. In accordance with the conventions of the Venn diagrams, the shaded area has no members.

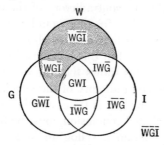

Now consider the minor premise:

All grampuses are whales. $g\bar{w} = 0$

Since there are no grampuses that are not whales, the area of the "grampus" circle that is outside the "whale" circle is shaded in. We shade in areas $G\overline{W}\overline{I}$ and $\overline{I}\overline{W}G$. (To distinguish the two shaded areas we use two different types of shading.)

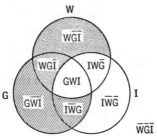

Now the validity of this syllogism can be tested and confirmed by inspection of the diagram. For, by diagraming the premises, we have also diagramed the conclusion:

All grampuses are introverts. $g\bar{\imath} = 0$

This conclusion states that there are no grampuses that are not introverts. But the diagram tells us exactly that. The area which would accommodate nonintroverted grampuses (the sum of areas $\overline{GWI}$, $\overline{WGI}$) is *shaded,* showing that it has no members.

Or put it this way. If the conclusion of the syllogism is false, then its contradictory "Some grampuses are not introverts" ($g\bar{\imath} \neq 0$) must be true. But this means that there is at least one member in the area reserved for nonintroverted grampuses. Could this contradictory of the original conclusion be diagramed? No, for this would require our putting an x or an asterisk in that area to show that at least one member existed there. But this is impossible, since the area is already shaded; this shows that there are no inhabitants in it. Thus, if the contradictory of the conclusion cannot be read from the diagram, it is false; and being false, *its* contradictory, the original conclusion, must be true.

Suppose we diagram a syllogism in DATISI (AII, third figure):

All bassoonists are temperamental.
Some bassoonists are Frenchmen.
∴ Some Frenchmen are temperamental.

We notice that this is a syllogism one of whose premises is a universal and the other a particular proposition. In diagraming such syllogisms, it is convenient to *diagram the universal premise first.* Since the major premise tells us that there are no bassoonists who are nontemperamental ($b\bar{t} = 0$), we shade in the appropriate area. And, since the minor premise informs us that there is at least one bassoonist who is a Frenchman ($bf \neq 0$), we place an x in the appropriate area. The region in which we place the x could not have been shaded, for the x means "there is at least one member here,"

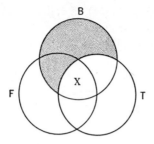

and shaded areas have no members. Now, having diagramed the premises, we may see by inspecting the diagram that the conclusion "Some Frenchmen are temperamental" is also diagramed. For there is an x in the area common to Frenchmen and those who are temperamental, meaning that there is at least one Frenchman who is temperamental.

Now let us construct a diagram for a syllogism in AOO, third figure:

All ghosts are vaporous.	$g\bar{v} = 0$
Some ghosts do not sing.	$g\bar{s} \neq 0$
∴ Some singers are not vaporous.	$s\bar{v} \neq 0$

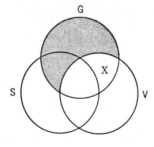

The major premise tells us that there are no nonvaporous ghosts ($g\bar{v} = 0$). So we shade the appropriate area to show absence of inhabitants. The minor informs us that there is at least one nonsinging ghost ($g\bar{s} \neq 0$). So we put an x in the appropriate area. Now we try to read off the conclusion from the diagramed premises. But we cannot. Why? The conclusion tells us that there is at least one singer who is not vaporous ($s\bar{v} \neq 0$); yet there is no x in the appropriate area (nonvaporous singer) to tell us that there is at least one inhabitant of that area.

Now let us try a syllogism in AII, second figure:

All koalas are gentle.
Some wombats are gentle.
∴ Some wombats are koalas.

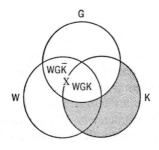

The major premise tells us that nongentle koalas do not exist ($k\bar{g} = 0$), so we shade in the appropriate area. The minor premise informs us that there is at least one gentle wombat ($wg \neq 0$). Where shall we put the x? It could go into either sector WGK̄ or WGK. But there is no further information to help us decide which. So we put the x on the *borderline* between WGK̄ and WGK. The premises now satisfactorily diagramed, we shall try to read the conclusion. But we find that we cannot. The conclusion informs us that there is at least one wombat which is at the same time a koala ($wk = 0$). But there is no x *inside* the unshaded area common to wombats and koalas to show that there is at least one wombat-koala. The x on the borderline shows no more than this—that there *could be* a wombat that is a koala. It does not show that there *is* one. Hence the conclusion cannot be read from the diagram of the premises, and the syllogism is invalid.

Finally, let us diagram the following syllogism:

All Irishmen are kings.
All Irishmen are wanderers.
∴ Some wanderers are kings.

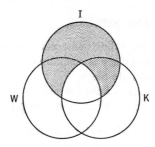

The diagram completed, we find that we cannot read off the conclusion. The conclusion states that there is at least one wanderer-king ($wk \neq 0$). But we find no x in the unshaded area reserved for wanderer-kings. It would seem that the syllogism is invalid, and so it is by Venn diagrams. But the syllogism is DARAPTI (AAI, third figure) and tests valid by the traditional rules. How is the discrepancy to be explained? The answer is that DARAPTI is one of the syllogisms with strengthened premises. Such syllogisms have two universal premises and a particular conclusion. Now, assuming the distinction between existential and nonexistential propositions (a distinction on which the Venn diagrams are based), then a particular conclusion *cannot* be derived validly from two general premises. "All Irishmen are kings" means only (on the Venn interpretation) that if there is an Irishman, then he is a king. "All Irishmen are wanderers" means only that if there is an Irishman, he is a wanderer. But the conclusion, "Some wanderers are kings," asserts the existence of at least one wanderer-king. And for this assertion of existence, the premises give no ground; they do not assert the existence of anything.

DARAPTI tests valid by the traditional rules and "common sense" because classical logic and ordinary usage generally assume the existential interpretation of general propositions. That is, when in ordinary discourse we say "All Irishmen have royal blood," we tacitly assume "And everybody knows there are Irishmen." Syllogisms with weakened conclusion will also fail to test "valid" by Venn diagrams. The reason is the same as above.

QUESTIONS AND EXERCISES

1. Test the following syllogisms according to traditional rules. If more than one fallacy is committed, note accordingly.

   1. All Bulgarians are Slavs.
      Some residents of Sofia are Slavs.
      ∴ Some residents of Sofia are Bulgarians.

   2. No ironing boards are for sale here.
      That which is for sale here is not to be found elsewhere.
      ∴ That which is to be found elsewhere is not ironing boards.

   3. Some tau mesons are pions.
      All tau mesons are atomic particles.
      ∴ Some atomic particles are pions.

   4. No buglers eat artichokes.
      All who eat artichokes eventually go mad.
      ∴ Some who eventually go mad are not buglers.

   5. Some anteaters do fine embroidery.
      All who do fine embroidery make good wives.
      ∴ Some who make good wives are anteaters.

   6. No admirers of Napoleon are lovers of the Bourbons.
      All admirers of Napoleon respect the Old Guard.
      ∴ None who respect the Old Guard are lovers of the Bourbons.

   7. Some redheads are not good-tempered.
      All Buddhist priests are good-tempered.
      ∴ Some Buddhist priests are not redheads.

   8. No pterodactyls live in the modern era.
      Some pterodactyls write letters to the *Times*.
      ∴ Some who write letters to the *Times* live in the modern era.

   9. None of the wounded are missing.
      Those who are missing are not identified.
      ∴ Some who are identified are not wounded.

   10. Some cuttlefish registered for library cards.
       None who registered for library cards are old residents.
       ∴ No old residents are cuttlefish.

11. All mental images are epiphenomena.
    All epiphenomena are phantasms.
    ∴ Some phantasms are not mental images.

12. All sharks bite.
    None who have lost their false teeth bite.
    ∴ Some who have lost their false teeth are not sharks.

13. Some baseball players are left-handed.
    None who are left-handed drink poison.
    ∴ No baseball players drink poison.

14. All quadrupeds can whistle.
    Some cats are quadrupeds.
    ∴ Some cats can whistle.

15. No sinners are allowed to enter heaven.
    Persons of unsound mind are not allowed to enter heaven.
    ∴ All sinners are persons of unsound mind.

16. Some holidays are rainy days.
    All rainy days are boring.
    ∴ Some holidays are boring.

17. No absentees are failed.
    All absentees receive a grade of zero.
    ∴ Some who receive a grade of zero are not failed.

18. Some people stick pins in babies.
    All people desire freedom of speech.
    ∴ Some who desire freedom of speech stick pins in babies.

19. None of the pre-Socratic philosophers write in prose.
    Those who write in prose are not poets.
    ∴ Some poets are not pre-Socratic philosophers.

20. Some reptiles are not good pets.
    All kittens are good pets.
    ∴ Some kittens are not reptiles.

2. Write down the 64 possible moods of the categorical syllogism, from AAA to OOO. With a pencil draw a line through as many moods as you can eliminate as invalid at sight by appeal to the traditional rules. It will not be necessary to

construct any syllogism. Compare your results with the twelve moods listed as "tentatively valid" on p. 51.

3. Construct your own syllogisms in the following moods. Test by traditional rules.

1. AAI, 3	6. IEO, 2
2. EIO, 4	7. AAA, 4
3. OAO, 2	8. AEE, 1
4. IAI, 1	9. AII, 4
5. AOO, 3	10. EAO, 3

4. Explain briefly why it is that syllogisms with weakened conclusion or strengthened premises cannot possibly commit the fallacy of the illicit minor. Show that syllogisms with weakened conclusions also have strengthened premises.

5. Why is it that when the minor term is predicate in the premise, the conclusion cannot be an A proposition?

6. Test the following by traditional rules. Test by Venn diagrams:

1. $a\bar{b} = 0$
   $c\bar{a} = 0$
   $\overline{c\bar{b} = 0}$

6. $ab \neq 0$
   $c\bar{b} = 0$
   $\overline{ca \neq 0}$

2. $a\bar{b} = 0$
   $b\bar{c} = 0$
   $\overline{c\bar{a} = 0}$

7. $a\bar{b} \neq 0$
   $a\bar{c} \neq 0$
   $\overline{c\bar{a} = 0}$

3. $ab = 0$
   $a\bar{c} = 0$
   $\overline{c\bar{b} \neq 0}$

8. $ab = 0$
   $c\bar{b} = 0$
   $\overline{ca = 0}$

4. $a\bar{b} = 0$
   $c\bar{a} = 0$
   $\overline{cb \neq 0}$

9. $ab = 0$
   $c\bar{b} = 0$
   $\overline{c\bar{a} \neq 0}$

5. $a\bar{b} = 0$
   $b\bar{c} \neq 0$
   $\overline{c\bar{a} \neq 0}$

10. $a\bar{b} = 0$
    $bc = 0$
    $\overline{ca = 0}$

7. Test the validity of the following syllogistic arguments:

1. "Gentlemen, this painting is undoubtedly the work of Paul Cézanne. See how the paint has been laid on layer over layer in thin brush strokes. You know that Cézanne applied his paint that way."

2. "It is impossible for members of the executive committee to be members of the social committee; for no members

of the social committee are members of the library committee, and every member of the library committee is a member of the executive committee.

3. "Liliana is obviously engaged, for she is wearing a diamond ring on the third finger of her left hand. And all engaged girls wear such rings."

4. "Some platinum wire does not conduct heat well, because all platinum wire has a high specific gravity, and some good heat conductors do not have a high specific gravity."

5. "Every Spanish boy dreams of marrying the perfect woman, and Carmen Sevilla is the perfect woman; hence, every Spanish boy dreams of marrying Carmen Sevilla.

6. "Barium salts do not have yellow spectroscopic lines. The reason is that only sodium salts have yellow spectroscopic lines, and barium salts are not sodium salts."

7. "The Haitian deity Damballa is transplanted from Dahomey, because Damballa is a voodoo god and all voodoo gods are transplanted from Dahomey."

8. "Mr. Fallico is not a charitable man, for during the year he has not given anything to the poor; and all charitable men during the course of a year give at least something to the poor."

9. "I tell you that a few of those who will escape eternal punishment are not among those who are born again. For all those who are born again are members of the elect, and there is no member of the elect who will not escape eternal punishment."

10. "At least a few of Mozart's contemporaries cannot have been his friends, for none of his friends wrote for clarinet, and those who wrote for clarinet are not Mozart's contemporaries."

5

The Syllogism (II)

Reduction of the "Imperfect" Figures of the Syllogism

We *reduce* a syllogism when we change it from second, third, or fourth figure into a valid and equivalent syllogism of the first figure. Classical logicians held that *all* valid syllogisms derived their validity from the axiom known as the dictum *de omni et nullo,* which states that "What is true of the universal (or class) is true of the particular (or subclass)"—or, the negative corollary, "What is untrue of the universal is untrue of the particular." Now syllogisms of the first figure plainly follow this axiom. This can be seen by comparing the pattern of any first-figure syllogism with the wording of the dictum. And if syllogisms of the first figure can be proved valid by showing that they follow the dictum, syllogisms which can be shown by reduction to be the *equivalents* of first-figure syllogisms are proved valid as well. Actually, there is no need to base the validity of a syllogism exclusively on the dictum. Indeed, as we shall see, classical logicians themselves showed by the process known as "indirect reduction" that it is quite possible to demonstrate the validity of a syllogism without appeal to this axiom. Nevertheless, reduction of the so-called "imperfect" figures of the syllogism to valid moods of the first figure is a useful logical exercise, as it furnishes us with still another means of testing the validity of syllogisms.

The Technique of Reduction

Valid syllogisms of the second, third, and fourth figures may be reduced to valid moods of the first figure by *converting* certain propositions of the syllogism and *transposing the premises* when necessary. For example, CAMESTRES (AEE, second figure) reduces to CELARENT

(EAE, first figure) by carrying out the following simple operations:

1. Transpose premises.
2. Convert original minor premise.
3. Convert conclusion.

Here is a syllogism in CAMESTRES:

All Chinese poets are delicate souls.
No boors are delicate souls.
_____
∴ No boors are Chinese poets.

Now here is the syllogism reduced to CELARENT:

No delicate souls are boors.
All Chinese poets are delicate souls.
_____
∴ No Chinese poets are boors.

Certain significant consonants in the code names of the syllogisms are helpful in performing reduction. The initial letter of the names of the second, third, and fourth figures tells which syllogism of the first figure the syllogism in question will reduce to. For example, CAMESTRES reduces to CELARENT, BRAMANTIP to BARBARA. More important, however, are the following significant consonants which are given below together with their meanings:

m (mutare)	Transpose premises.
s (simpliciter)	Convert preceding proposition *simply* (that is, like an E or an I proposition).
p (per accidens)	Convert preceding proposition *per accidens* (that is, like an A proposition).

By following such hints, we may see that FESTINO can be reduced to FERIO (by converting the major), DISAMIS to DARII (by transposing the premises, converting the original major and conclusion), and so on.

Reduction of BAROCO and BOCARDO

In order to reduce these two syllogisms (AOO, second figure; and OAO, third figure), it is necessary to employ obversion. Now in ages past the use of obversion in reduction was frowned on for reasons that need not concern us here; but there is no reason why at our stage we cannot reduce these syllogisms, using obversion as needed. If the use of obversion is permitted, however, we shall need new code names for these two syllogisms and one new significant consonant:

k Obvert the preceding proposition.

The new code names are FAKSOKO and DOKSAMOKS. Since k means "Obvert the preceding proposition," and s means "convert," the combination ks will stand for "Give the partial contraposition of the preceding proposition." Here then is FAKSOKO (the old BAROCO, AOO, second figure):

> All librarians are faculty.
> Some staff are not faculty.
> ∴ Some staff are not librarians.

Replacing the major (an A proposition) by its partial contraposition (ks), and replacing the minor (the first O proposition) by its obverse (k), we obtain the following syllogism in FERIO (EIO, first figure):

> No nonfaculty are librarians.
> Some staff are nonfaculty.
> ∴ Some staff are not librarians.

DOKSAMOKS (the old BOKARDO, OAO, third figure) may be reduced to DARII by transposing the premises (M), and replacing both O propositions by their partial contrapositions (ks).

The "Indirect" Reduction of BAROCO and BOCARDO

Classical logicians of olden days refused to recognize the validity of the reductions of BAROCO (FAKSOKO) and BOCARDO (DOKSAMOKS) as given above. Such reductions involved obversion, to which they objected. Unable to show, therefore, that these two syllogisms followed the dictum, and hence unable to demonstrate their validity by appeal to this basic axiom, classical logicians devised an independent way of demonstrating the validity of syllogisms which dispensed with appeal to the dictum. This is done by the method of demonstration *per impossibile*—that is, by showing that any assumption of the *invalidity* of BAROCO and BOCARDO is impossible. This method is known as "indirect reduction," a misleading name, for the process is not reduction at all, but an independent method of demonstrating the validity of syllogisms; it constitutes a fourth testing procedure for validity.

First let us concede that *if* it can be shown that, *given* the truth of the premises of a syllogism, the truth of its conclusion necessarily follows, *then* the syllogism is valid. We can have no doubt of this, for it is in this way that syllogistic reasoning is defined. Now here is BAROCO (AOO, second figure):

All Italians love music.
Some Tunisians do not love music.
∴ Some Tunisians are not Italians.

Given: the two premises as true.
To prove: "Some Tunisians are not Italians" must be true.

1. Suppose the conclusion "Some Tunisians are not Italians" is *false*. Then its contradictory, "All Tunisians are Italians," must be true. For, of two contradictories, one must be true, the other false.

2. Take this contradictory of the original conclusion and combine it with the *major premise* of the original syllogism:

All Italians love music.
All Tunisians are Italians.

What follows?

All Tunisians love music.

3. But this new conclusion, "All Tunisians love music," cannot be true, for it contradicts the original minor which was given as true.

4. Now if "All Tunisians love music" is false, then "All

Tunisians are Italians" is also false, since it was given as
true in the original major that "All Italians love music."

5. If "All Tunisians are Italians" is false, then its contradictory, "Some Tunisians are not Italians," must be true.
For, of two contradictories, one must be true, the other
false. Q.E.D.

This "indirect" method of demonstrating the validity of
syllogisms may also be applied to BOCARDO. (In the second
step, combine the contradictory of the conclusion with the
original *minor*.) In fact, the validity of any syllogism of the
second, third, and fourth figure may be tested in this way.

The Antilogism

The antilogism is actually an abbreviated form of the
procedure used in indirect reduction. *It is a syllogism
whose conclusion has been replaced by its contradictory.*
Developed by Christine Ladd-Franklin, the antilogism or
"inconsistent triad" is a device to test syllogisms without
using the traditional rules.

The antilogism of every valid syllogism must meet three
conditions:

1. It has two universal propositions and one particular
proposition, or (symbolically) two equations (=) and
one inequation (≠).

2. The two equations have a common term which occurs
once affirmatively and once negatively.

3. The inequation will contain the other terms.

For example, let us take a syllogism in BARBARA (AAA,
first figure), and place beside each of its propositions the
equivalent Venn propositional formula (null form):

All petty officers are enlisted men.	$a\bar{b} = 0$
All gunner's mates are petty officers.	$c\bar{a} = 0$
∴ All gunner's mates are enlisted men.	$c\bar{b} = 0$

Replacing the conclusion with its contradictory, we get
the following antilogism:

All petty officers are enlisted men.	$a\bar{b} = 0$
All gunner's mates are petty officers.	$c\bar{a} = 0$
∴ Some gunner's mates are not enlisted men.	$c\bar{b} \neq 0$

The antilogism thus obtained meets the three conditions required, and hence the syllogism from which it is derived is valid. Here is a second example, this time OAO, second figure:

Some mysogynists are not married.	$a\bar{b} \neq 0$
All of my brothers are married.	$c\bar{b} = 0$
∴ Some of my brothers are not misogynists.	$c\bar{a} \neq 0$

Replacing the conclusion with its contradictory, we obtain the following antilogism:

Some misognynists are not married.	$a\bar{b} \neq 0$
All of my brothers are married.	$c\bar{b} = 0$
∴ All of my brothers are misognyists.	$c\bar{a} = 0$

The syllogism is invalid. While the first condition for a valid antilogism is met, the second is not. There is a term common to the equations, but it does not occur once affirmatively and once negatively.

We should note that the antilogism will not work with syllogisms with strengthened or weakened conclusions. Such syllogisms, when tested by antilogism, register "invalid," unless at least one of the general premises is interpreted existentially, that is, as an inequation.

IRREGULAR AND COMPOUND FORMS OF THE CATEGORICAL SYLLOGISM

Enthymemes

An enthymeme is a categorical syllogism with one of its propositions unexpressed. Syllogistic reasoning in ordinary conversation most often takes this form. Enthymemes are said to be of the *first order* when the *major* premise in unexpressed:

Diamonds are costly, for they are rare.

The implicit syllogism here is:

What is rare is costly.
Diamonds are rare.
∴ Diamonds are costly.

In enthymemes of the *second order,* the *minor* premise
is unexpressed:

> That yawl has running lights, because all
> sailing vessels are required to have them.

The complete syllogism is:

> All sailing vessels are required to have running lights.
> That yawl is a sailing vessel.
> ───────────────────────────────
> ∴ That yawl is required to have running lights.

Enthymemes of the first and second order show how in
ordinary conversation we present our *conclusions first* and
then support them with premises. This contrasts with the
formal syllogism, which presents its premises first and its
conclusion last. Another way of putting this is to say that
the arrangement of propositions in the formal syllogism
represents the *order of proof,* while the arrangement of
propositions in the enthymeme represents the *order of
discovery.* This holds, however, only for enthymemes of
the first and second order. In third-order enthymemes,
the conclusion is unexpressed, while both premises are
stated. In the following news extract, there is an implicit
third-order enthymeme:

> In the midst of an interchange on the President's request for
> power to control speculation on the commodity exchanges, a
> correspondent broke in. "Would these controls," he asked, "re-
> late also to the cotton and wool exchanges?" The President
> looked at his interrogator. "Is cotton a commodity?" he asked.
> "Is wool a commodity?" "They are generally so considered, sir,"
> replied the correspondent. "All right, then, that answers the
> question," the President retorted.

Sorites

A sorites is a compound syllogism consisting of a
chain of incompletely expressed syllogisms. It may be one
of several related forms, of which the following is the most
obvious:

All A's are B's.	All Concord farmers are New Englanders.
All B's are C's.	All New Englanders are Yankees.
All C's are D's.	All Yankees are patriots.
All D's are E's.	All patriots will fight for their country.
∴ All A's are E's.	∴ All Concord farmers will fight for their country.

A sorites of this type can be carried on to any length provided its arrangement is consecutive, so that each term except the first and last (here, A and E) occurs twice, once as subject and once as predicate.

More interesting sorites (more difficult too) are set forth by C. L. Dodgson ("Lewis Carroll") in his *Symbolic Logic* (*16*).[1] Here the author of *Alice in Wonderland* offers sets of propositions for premises and asks the reader to draw the conclusion. For example, find the conclusion of:

1. Babies are illogical;
2. Nobody is despised who can manage a crocodile;
3. Illogical persons are despised.

Treating each term as a class (using circle diagrams as an aid), we may draw the conclusion "Babies cannot manage crocodiles." Here is another set of premises the conclusion for which we are asked to find:

1. No interesting poems are unpopular among people of real taste;
2. No modern poetry is free from affectation;
3. All *your* poems are on the subject of soap bubbles;
4. No affected poetry is popular among people of real taste;
5. No ancient poem is on the subject of soap bubbles.

The conclusion drawn is "All *your* poems are uninteresting." Further examples of Lewis Carroll's sorites may be found in the exercises at the end of this chapter.

A sorites may also occur in implicative, or "if . . . then . . . ," form. (The symbol ⊃ stands for "if . . . then . . . ," the dot · for "and"):

[1] Numbers in parentheses refer to the General Bibliography, p. 215, where details of publication are given.

$$\frac{p \supset q \cdot q \supset r \cdot r \supset s \cdot s \supset t}{p \supset t}$$

(If p, then q; and if q, then r; and if r, then s; and if, s then t; therefore, if p, then t.) Here is an implicative sorites (though not one in strict form) from the precepts of the ancient Chinese philosopher Confucius, who is urging the "Rectification of the Names":

If names be not correct, language is not in accordance with the truth of things.

If language is not in accordance with the truth of things, affairs cannot be carried on to success.

If affairs cannot be carried on to success, proprieties and music will not flourish.

If proprieties and music do not flourish, punishments will not be properly awarded.

If punishments are not properly awarded, the people do not know how to move hand or foot.

Therefore, a superior man considers it necessary that the names he uses may be spoken appropriately.[2]

An implicative sorites is present in the following passage from Shakespeare's *As You Like It*. Says Touchstone:

Why, if thou never wast at court, thou never sawest good manners. If thou never sawest good manners, then thy manner must be wicked, and wickedness is sin, and sin is damnation. Thou art in a parlous state, shepherd.[3]

CONDITIONAL SYLLOGISMS

Hypothetical or Implicative Syllogisms

The hypothetical or implicative syllogism is one in which the major premise is a compound proposition of the implicative ("if . . . then . . .") type:

If the patient has fever, he is infected.
The patient has fever.

∴ He is infected.

[2] Analects XIII, 3. Such sorites are common in later Confucian literature. According to sinologue Arthur Waley, the links in chain arguments of this kind were intended as rhetorical rather than logical.

[3] *As You Like It*, Act III, Scene ii.

In such syllogisms, the "if" clause is called the *antecedent,* and the "then" clause is called the *consequent.* There are only two valid moods of the implicative syllogism. In the first, *modus ponens,* the antecedent is affirmed. In the second, *modus tollens,* the consequent is denied. The affirming or denying is done in the minor premise.

1. *Modus ponens:*
   If his name's Jim Hagerty, he's an Irishman.
   His name is Jim Hagerty.
   ∴ He is an Irishman.
2. *Modus tollens:*
   If there is a light in the tower, the British are coming.
   The British are not coming.
   ∴ There is not a light in the tower.

The moods, rules, and fallacies of the implicative syllogism may be summarily presented thus:

Moods: (1) *Modus ponens* (in which the antecedent is affirmed).
   (2) *Modus tollens* (in which the consequent is denied).
Rules: (1) Either—the antecedent must be affirmed.
   (2) Or—the consequent must be denied.
Fallacies: (1) Affirming the consequent.
   (2) Denying the antecedent.

Here is an example of *affirming the consequent:*

   If wages are high, prices rise.
   Prices are rising.
   ∴ Wages are high.

And here is an instance of the fallacy of *denying the antecedent:*

   If Bill Nietman is a Princeton graduate, he cuts his own hair.
   Bill Nietman is not a Princeton graduate.
   ∴ He does not cut his own hair.

We should note that hypothetical ("if . . . then . . .") syllogisms can easily be recast in the form of their categorical equivalents. If we do this, we see that the categorical equivalent of a syllogism which affirms the consequent commits the fallacy of the undistributed middle; and that the categorical equivalent of a syllogism denying the antecedent commits the fallacy of illicit process of the major. An illustration of the first case would be:

> If a salesman attempts to sell overshoes to water buffaloes he gets small thanks for his pains.
> This salesman gets small thanks for his pains.
> ___
> ∴ This salesman attempts to sell overshoes to water buffaloes.

> All salesmen who attempt to sell overshoes to water buffaloes get small thanks for their pains.
> This salesman gets small thanks for his pains.
> ___
> ∴ This salesman attempts to sell overshoes to water buffaloes.

If we let "p" stand for the antecedent, "q" for the consequent, "$\supset$" for "if . . . then . . . ," and "$-$" for "not," we may easily show the structure of all four types of implicative syllogisms in symbolic notation:

A. *Modus ponens*

$$p \supset q$$
$$\frac{p}{q} \qquad \text{valid}$$

B. *Modus tollens*

$$p \supset q$$
$$\frac{-q}{-p} \qquad \text{valid}$$

C. Affirming the consequent

$$p \supset q$$
$$\frac{q}{p} \qquad \text{invalid}$$

C. Denying the antecedent

$$p \supset q$$
$$\frac{-p}{-q} \qquad \text{invalid}$$

There is a sense of "if" stricter than that illustrated above. This is "if and only if," and a proposition in which it appears is known as a *biconditional*. When the major premise of an implicative syllogism is a biconditional proposition, all four forms illustrated in the previous paragraph are valid. Using the symbol $\equiv$ for "if and only if," the schemas for these valid forms are:

A. $p \equiv q$
$$\frac{p}{q}$$

B. $\quad p \equiv q$
$$\frac{-q}{-p}$$

C. $p \equiv q$
$$\frac{q}{p}$$

D. $\quad p \equiv q$
$$\frac{-p}{-q}$$

Thus there is no fallacy in the following:

> If (and only if) you are rich, will I marry you.
> I'll marry you.
> ───────────────────────────
> ∴ You are rich.

> If (and only if) a wart hog wants perfume, he uses *L'Exstase*.
> This wart hog does not want perfume.
> ───
> ∴ He is not using *L'Exstase*.

Alternative and Disjunctive Syllogisms

Alternative and disjunctive syllogisms have for their major premises alternative and disjunctive propositions respectively. Both these compound propositions are of the "either . . . or . . ." type. The difference between them is this: (1) Alternative propositions signify "either . . . or . . . *and possibly both.*" (2) Disjunctive propositions signify "either . . . or . . . *and not both.*" In ordinary discourse most of our "either . . . or's . . ." are disjunctive; that is, they have "not both" tacitly tacked on, as in the case of "Today is either Monday or Tuesday." But occasionally we use "either . . . or . . ." in the broad or inclusive sense in conversation. Denial of this produces the fallacy in the third example below. We shall assume that "either . . . or . . ." means "either . . . or . . . and possibly both," unless the proposition in question is explicitly disjunctive. The symbol for alternation is "$\lor$." Here are four types of alternative syllogisms:

A. Either I shall speak to his sister
   or I shall visit his home. $p \lor q$
   ───────────────────────── $-p$
   I shall not speak to his sister.   ───────
   ∴ I shall visit his home. q valid

B. Either mother is laughing or she's
   crying. $p \lor q$
   ───────────────────── $-q$
   She's not crying.   ───────
   ∴ She's laughing. p valid

C. Either Betsy will help or Leilani $p \lor q$ invalid
   will help. p
   ────────────────────────   ───────
   Betsy will help. $-q$
   ∴ Leilani will not help.

D. Either the conductor checks $p \lor q$
    tickets here or he checks q
    them after Jamaica.

He checks tickets after Jamaica. $-p$ invalid

∴ He doesn't check them here.

The disjunctive syllogism has a disjunctive proposition for its major premise. Such a proposition states that either one or the other of two alternatives (or "disjuncts") is true, but not *both:*

> Either a man's married or he's a bachelor (and not both).
> This man is married.
>
> He is not a bachelor.

The four alternative syllogisms listed above may be turned into disjunctive syllogisms simply by adding the phrase "and not both" to the major premise. Symbolically, each major premise would then be set down as:

$$[p \lor q] \cdot [-(p \cdot q)]$$

(Either p or q is true, and it is not the case that p and q both are true.)

or more simply, using the symbol for disjunction,

$$p \land q$$

With such a major premise, all four schemas above will be valid.

The Dilemma

The dilemma, a classic device of oratory, is an argument in which the speaker presents his opponent with two alternatives, forcing him to choose between them, so that whichever alternative he chooses, the result will be disadvantageous to him. For example:

> If you allow Catiline to remain alive, you will live in constant danger; and if you put him to death, you will violate the law.
>
> But either you allow Catiline to remain alive or you put him to death.
>
> Therefore, either you will live in constant danger or you will violate the law.

The logical structure of a dilemma in interesting. The major premise is a conjunction of implicative ("if . . . then . . .") propositions, and the minor an alternation either of the antecedents of the two implicative propositions or of the negations (contradictories) of their consequents. The dilemma is said to be *constructive* when the minor affirms one or other of the antecedents; it is said to be *destructive* when it denies one or other of the consequents.

Constructive	*Destructive*
$(p \supset q) \cdot (r \supset s)$	$(p \supset q) \cdot (r \supset s)$
$p \lor r$	$-q \lor -s$
$\therefore q \lor s$	$\therefore -p \lor -r$

The dilemma against Catiline is an example of the first form. An illustration of the second would be:

> If I am to make Mother happy, I must marry Bill; and if I am to make Tom happy, I must marry *him*.
> Either I won't marry Bill or I won't marry Tom.
> Therefore, I am going to make either Mother or Tom unhappy.

Dilemmas may be rebutted in more than one way. For example, suppose we urge the following argument:

> If the defendant was in the victim's apartment, he had opportunity to kill him; and if the defendant was in the victim's office, he had opportunity to kill him.
> Either the defendant was in the victim's apartment or in his office.
> Therefore, he had opportunity to kill him.

Our opponent may try to show that in our minor premise we have not exhausted all the alternatives. "The defendant could have been in Mario's Bar and Grill," he may say, and if he is successful in proving it, showing that in the grill there was no opportunity to kill the victim, our opponent "escapes between the horns" of the dilemma. The following dilemma cannot be rebutted by "escaping between the horns," for the alternatives presented in the minor are exhaustive. There is a story that the Roman emperor Trajan posted edicts to the effect that his soldiers should not seek out Christians; but if the latter forced themselves upon the notice of the soldiers, they should be arrested and punished. Now Tertullian offered the following argument against this:

If the Christians are guilty of crime, they should be sought out; and if they are innocent of crime, they should not be punished at all.

But either they are guilty or innocent of crime.

Therefore, either they should be sought out (which the edict forbids) or they should not be punished under any circumstance (this is also contrary to the edict).

A well-known way to dodge the horns of a dilemma is to substitute the contradictory for each consequent in the major premise, and draw a different conclusion, by changing their places. Suppose we have:

$$(p \supset q) \cdot (r \supset s)$$
$$\underline{p \lor r}$$
$$\therefore q \lor s$$

We may retort:

$$(p \supset -s) \cdot (r \supset -q)$$
$$\underline{p \lor r}$$
$$-s \lor -q$$

The best-known example of such a retort occurs in the story of the Athenian mother and her son who wanted to go into politics. The mother did her best to dissuade her son, saying, "If you go into politics and are just, men will hate you; and if you are unjust, the gods will hate you. You must either act justly or unjustly. So in either case you will be hated." To which the son replied, "Mother, by your own argument, I *should* go into politics. For, if I am just, the gods will love me; and if I am unjust, men will love me. So in either case I will be loved." The son's retort, of course, does not disprove his mother's argument, for the two conclusions could be true at the same time. As C. A. Mace remarks, such a retort seems to be merely a formal device for looking on the bright side of things.

RELATIONAL ARGUMENTS

Transitive and Intransitive Relations

We realize that propositions which show a relation of class inclusion or exclusion between the classes signified by the subject and predicate terms form but a part of the large stock of propositional types. Consider the statement form:

$$x \text{ is greater than } y$$

Here the two terms, x and y, are connected in a relationship obviously different from that of class inclusion or exclusion. But quasi-syllogistic arguments can easily be constructed which use such propositional forms. For example:

x is greater than y.
y is greater than z.
∴ x is greater than z.

If Victoria is greater than George, and George is greater than Edward, then Victoria is greater than Edward. Symbolically:

$$V \ R \ G$$
$$G \ R \ E$$
$$\therefore V \ R \ E$$

But is the following argument valid?

Cézanne is a friend of Zola.
Zola is a friend of Huysmans.
∴ Cézanne is a friend of Huysmans.

No, this argument is not valid, because the relation "a friend of" is *nontransitive*. For such an argument to be valid, the relationship between the two terms must be *transitive*, as in this case:

Adam is an ancestor of Abraham.
Abraham is an ancestor of Joseph.
∴ Adam is an ancestor of Joseph.

The relation "is an ancestor of" is, of course, transitive. Similarly, we may argue validly that since Rome is warmer than Paris, and Paris is warmer than Moscow, therefore Rome is warmer than Moscow. But we may not argue that since Isaac begat Jacob and Jacob begat Esau, therefore Isaac begat Esau. The relation "begat" is *intransitive*.

In examining such relational arguments drawn from ordinary language, we cannot tell by purely formal means whether the relations concerned are transitive or intransitive. Familiarity with ordinary linguistic usage is necessary if we are to label "is greater than" transitive, and "is a child of" intransitive. But once it is determined that R is a transitive relation, we may conclude that *a* has the relation of R to *c* if *a* has the relation of R to *b*, and *b* has the relation of R to *c*. For it is thus that transitivity is *defined*.

The copula of the classical two-term class-inclusion proposition is itself an obvious example of a transitive relation. It is this relation which makes possible the classical syllogism. In the propositions:

> Sea cucumbers are holuthurians.
> Holuthurians are echinoderms.

the copula "are" is interpreted as "are members of the class of," and thus we are able to draw the conclusion:

> Sea cucumbers are echinoderms.

A distinction may also be drawn between *symmetrical* and *asymmetrical* relations. A symmetrical relation is reciprocal; it is a relation such that if *a* has the relation of *R* to *b*, then *b* has the relation of *R* to *a*. The relation "is a roommate of" is symmetrical; so is "is the spouse of," and "is the coreligionist of." An asymmetrical relation is not reciprocal. Knowing that *a* has the relation of *R* to *b*, I cannot infer from this that *b* has the relation of *R* to *a*. "Is smoother than" is certainly asymmetrical, as are the relations "is colder than" and "is the wife of."

BIBLIOGRAPHICAL NOTE

Excellent treatments of syllogistic logic, including the classical analysis of propositions, are found in many texts. An old favorite is Jevons' *Elementary Lessons in Logic* (25). More modern and advanced treatments are offered in Keynes, *Formal Logic* (27); Mace, *The Principles of Logic* (31); Eaton, *General Logic* (19); Cohen and Nagel, *Introduction to Logic and Scientific Method* (11).

The samples of Lewis Carroll's sorites in the text and chapter exercises are taken from his *Symbolic Logic* (16). Despite the title of his book, Carroll's work in logic is mainly concerned with the syllogistic variety; either he did not know or was not interested in the revolutionary work of his contemporary, George Boole. However, the author of *Alice in Wonderland* devised many ingenious logical diagrams and illustrations, and invented a logical game played with colored counters (*The Game of Logic* [15]).

QUESTIONS AND EXERCISES

1. Reduce the following to valid syllogisms of the first figure:

1. All psychiatrists are physicians.
   Some psychoanalysts are not physicians.
   ∴ Some psychoanalysts are not psychiatrists.

2. No inert gases are flammable.
   All inert gases are elements.
   ∴ Some elements are not flammable.

3. Some philosophers are moralists.
   All moralists are reformers.
   ∴ Some reformers are philosophers.

4. All crude oils are petroleum products.
   No watchmakers' oils are petroleum products.
   ∴ No watchmakers' oils are crude oils.

5. All dolls have mortal souls.
   All dolls are sound sleepers.
   ∴ Some sound sleepers have mortal souls.

6. No elephants sing.
   Some elephants dance.
   ∴ Some that dance do not sing.

7. All cheese salesmen have records as subversives.
   None who have records as subversives will be allowed to own bicycles.
   ∴ None who will be allowed to own bicycles are cheese salesmen.

2. Construct a syllogism in OAO, third figure, and demonstrate its validity by the method of "indirect reduction." Use as terms those listed below:

    Major: cassowaries who are able to solve the binomial theorem.

    Minor: those required to take an intelligence test before marriage.

    Middle: those entitled to knowledge and the free use thereof.

3. Construct syllogisms as follows, and reduce to the first figure:

    1. OAO, third figure
    2. EIO, second figure
    3. AAI, fourth figure
    4. EAE, second figure
    5. AEE, fourth figure

4. Test the following syllogisms by antilogism. (Put all propositions into Venn null forms.)

    1. Some gentlemen prefer blondes.
       All gentlemen take off their hats when addressing a rhinoceros.
       ∴ Some who take off their hats when addressing a rhinoceros do not prefer blondes.

    2. No logic machines are accurate.
       All truth-function evaluators are logic machines.
       ∴ No truth-function evaluators are accurate.

    3. No television performers eat graham crackers.
       All babies eat graham crackers.
       ∴ Some babies are not television performers.

    4. All trains that stop at Wantagh are trains that stop at Seaford.
       No trains that stop at Jamaica are trains that stop at Wantagh.
       ∴ No trains that stop at Jamaica are trains that stop at Seaford.

    5. No keepers of giant pandas want to look after baby hippos.
       Some discontented bear trainers want to look after baby hippos.
       ∴ Some discontented bear trainers are not keepers of giant pandas.

6. Some husbands beat their wives with a large stick.
   All husbands pour oatmeal on their children.
   ∴ Some who pour oatmeal on their children beat their
   wives with a large stick.

7. No members of the PTA are allowed to sell narcotics.
   Druggists are allowed to sell narcotics.
   ∴ No druggists are members of the PTA.

8. All Toscanini recordings are Red Seal records.
   All Red Seal records cost at least two dollars.
   ∴ Some things that cost at least two dollars are To-
   scanini recordings.

9. No long-haired sheep are wanted for purchase.
   Some long-haired sheep are not too old to dream.
   ∴ Some who are too old to dream are not wanted for
   purchase.

10. Every soldier of the Emperor carries a marshal's baton
    in his knapsack.
    Every man in the Imperial Army is a soldier of the
    Emperor.
    ∴ Every man in the Imperial Army carries a marshal's
    baton in his knapsack.

5. The eight Beatitudes in the Sermon on the Mount are enthymemes. Look them up in the New Testament, and construct equivalent categorical syllogisms for each.

6. Draw conclusions from each of the following proposed by
Lewis Carroll as premises of sorites (circle diagrams will
help):

1. My saucepans are the only things I have that are made of
   tin;
   I find all *your* presents very useful;
   None of my saucepans are of the slightest use.

2. No ducks waltz;
   No officers ever decline to waltz;
   All my poultry are ducks.

3. There are no pencils of mine in this box;
   No sugar plums of mine are cigars;
   The whole of my property that is not in this box consists
   of cigars.

4. All unripe fruit is unwholesome;
   All these apples are wholesome;
   No fruit, grown in the shade, is ripe.

5. The only articles of food that my doctor allows me are such as are not very rich;
   Nothing that agrees with me is unsuitable for supper;
   Wedding cake is always very rich;
   My doctor allows me all articles of food that are suitable for supper.

7. Construct two implicative syllogisms, using your own subject matter, such that one commits the fallacy of affirming the consequent and the other commits the fallacy of denying the antecedent. Now construct equivalent categorical syllogisms, and show what violation of the traditional rules occurs in each case.

8. Put the following arguments into symbolic notation, and test for validity:

1. "That madman! Has he had a picture acepted by the Academy? No! Now you admit, do you not, that if a painter's pictures are accepted by the Academy, he is at least a competent artist? Good. The implication is obvious. This man Seurat is quite the reverse of a competent artist."

2. "If your friend Ruth looks like Lilli Palmer, she is beautiful. But you say she does not look like Lilli Palmer. Alas, then your friend Ruth is not beautiful."

3. "If and only if the priest is wearing red vestments, the Mass is for a martyr. Now we know that this Mass is for a martyr. Therefore we know that the priest is wearing red vestments."

4. "The dormouse has not buried the worm, for if he had buried it the worm would be dead, and the worm is not dead."

5. "Of course, this man is married, for if a man is married he has a wife, and this man has a wife."

6. "That orangutan is *not* irritated. How do I know? Listen, my friend, if a orangutan is irritated, it growls, and this orangutang *is not growling*."

7. "Either you are keeping a pterodactyl in the bathtub or you are meeting secretly with a cipher clerk from the embassy. It is impossible that you can be doing both. Now we have found out that you have been meeting secretly with a cipher clerk from the embassy. It is evident, therefore, that you are not keeping a pterodactyl in the bathtub."

8. "Either she loved me or she was deceiving me. I have confirmed that fact that she loved me. So I know she was not deceiving me."

9. "It can't be that the train has passed. If the train has passed, the green flag is up, and the green flag is not up."

10. "Either it's raining or it's not raining. It's not raining. Therefore, it's raining."

9. Once a crocodile stole a baby from a mother who was washing clothes along the banks of the Ganges. In answer to her pleas, the crocodile promised to return the baby if the mother would give the right answer to this question: Is the crocodile going to restore the baby? The mother said, "The answer is no. Now you must keep your promise; if the answer is wrong, that must mean you are going to give back the baby anyway. If it is right, you must keep your promise. In either case, you must give me back the baby."

But the crocodie answered, "If no is the right answer, what makes it right is that I am not going to give back the baby; if it is the wrong answer, then my promise does not hold. In either case, I am not going to restore the baby."

How would a wise and just judge decide the dispute?

10. A New York professor, testifying before an investigating committee of the United States Senate in 1952, invoked the privilege against self-incrimination under the Fifth Amendment of the Constitution of the United States, and was summarily discharged from his position as professor at B_____ College. In its decision on the case, dated April 9, 1956, the United States Supreme Court summarized the argument of the New York City Board of Education against the professor as follows:

"Here the board in support of its position contends that only two possible inferences flow from appellant's claim of self-incrimination: (1) that the answering of the question ('Were you a member of the Communist Party during 1940 and 1941?') would tend to prove him guilty of a crime in some way connected with his official conduct; or (2) that in order to avoid answering the question he falsely invoked the privilege by stating that the answer would tend to incriminate him, and thus committed perjury. Either inference, it [the Board] insists, is sufficient to justify the termination of his employment."

Put the argument of the Board of Education in the form of a dilemma. Are the alternatives exhausted in the minor premise? If not, what third alternative could serve to rebut the argument?

11. I am informed that Napa is north of San Francisco, and that San Francisco is west of Oakland. I conclude that therefore Napa is northwest of Oakland. But when I examine a map of California to check this, I see that Napa is actually northeast of Oakland. Was my relational syllogism invalid? If not, where lies the error?

12. Put the argument in the first paragraph of this book in syllogistic form.

6

Truth Functions

From our work on various types of conditional syllogisms, we have seen how easily the forms of compound propositions can be represented in modern symbolic notation. We must now look more closely at these propositional forms in order to analyze them in a way unfamiliar to classical logicians. These compound forms belong to a type of expression logicians call *truth functions*. A truth function is an expression whose *truth value* (truth or falsity) is completely determined by the truth values of its component propositions. For example, the truth of the compound proposition:

The earth is flat and the end of the world is at hand.

is a function of (i.e., depends on the truth of) its component simple propositions (1) "The earth is flat," (2) "The end of the world is at hand." That is, the truth value of the propositional form:

p and *q*

depends on the individual truth values of *p* and *q* taken separately.

In dealing with truth functions, we may distinguish between *constants* and *variables*. In the expression:

either *p* or *q*

the "*p*" and the "*q*" are *variables* for simple propositions. (See above, Chapter 1, p. 4). Because they are variables or "blank spaces," we may replace "*p*" or "*q*" with any propositions we please. Thus "either *p* or *q*" could stand for:

Either you are insolent or you are ignorant.

or

> Either Titian painted this picture or the experts have been mistaken.

The logical form is not affected by the change in subject matter. The "either . . . or . . . " remains unchanged in both the above examples, and thus it is called a *constant*. In sum, variables are elements for which substitutions may be made; constants are elements whose meaning does not change no matter what propositions are substituted for the variables.

Let us look first at five common statement connectives, that is, constants by means of which we may combine simple propositions to form truth-functional compounds:

1. Negation   —   not
2. Conjunction   ·   and
3. Alternation   ∨   or
4. Implication   ⊃   if . . . then
5. Biconditional ≡   if and only if

We have met all these constants in previous chapters; we shall now proceed to define them more precisely.

1. Negation   −p

We may read this "not p" or "it is not the case that p." For the p in $-p$ we may substitute any declarative sentence, and then read $-p$ in either of these ways:

> It is not the case that Graham Greene is an American.
> Graham Greene is not an American.

Logically speaking, negation is absolutely basic. Logical systems for truth functions can be constructed successfully even if we dispense with certain common connectives such as implication and alternation, but we cannot get along without negation. The negation of any expression changes the truth value of that expression from "true" to "false," unless of course the expression is already false; in this case negation changes the truth value of the expression to "true." The negation of p is $-p$; the negation of $-p$ is $-(-p)$.

In most logical systems, classical or modern, only two truth values "true" and "false" are used. Hence these systems are often called "two-valued logics." It is possible to construct *many-valued* logics in which truth values are more complex than the simple binary "true-false" of the conventional systems. In recent years, interesting work has been done on multivalued logics, but this field is still difficult and unusual.

Let us construct a little *truth table* for negation which will show us the truth values of $-p$ when p is true and when p is false:

p	$-p$
T	F
F	T

2. Conjunction $p \cdot q$

We may read this simply "p and q." Since p and q are variables, we know that we may as usual substitute simple statements for them:

> Dragons crooned in the forest and ghosts whistled in the wind.

Logical conjunction is taken in a sense rather broader than "and" in ordinary conversation. In common discourse, the two sentences joined by the "and" are often causally connected, as in:

> Pat's father is a rancher and she lives in Montana.

But for logical purposes, when we assert $p \cdot q$ we simply assert p and q jointly. A perfectly satisfactory conjunction is:

> Beethoven wrote the Archduke Trio
> and four people tripped over that milk bottle.

Indeed, the logical sense of all these connectives—"not," "and," "or," "if," and "if and only if"—tends to vary from their sense in ordinary language. Hence we *define* the uses of the symbols $-$, $\cdot$, $\vee$, $\supset$, and $\equiv$ by the truth tables given for them. The defined uses of these symbols are in some cases distant, in some cases close to the corresponding ex-

pressions in ordinary usage. We shall, however, continue
to *read* them in ordinary English in the way we have been
doing.

Now let us make a truth table for our conjunctive function
$p \cdot q$. When p is true and q is true, then "p and q" is true.
But when p is false and q is true, then "p and q" cannot be
true. The same situation holds when p is true and q is false.
In the fourth case, too, when p is false and q is false, then
"p and q" must also be false. In tabular form:

p	q	$p \cdot q$
T	T	T
F	T	F
T	F	F
F	F	F

This truth table may be written in more compact form.
Simply write down the expression as a whole (in this case
$p \cdot q$), then write out the truth value of p and q, taken
separately, under those letters; and finally write down the
truth values for $p \cdot q$ under the dot which stands for "and."
This column then becomes the *main column* of the truth
table:

p	$\cdot$	q
T	T	T
F	F	T
T	F	F
F	F	F

We should notice that the denial of a conjunction is not
quite the same thing as a denial of each conjunct. $-(p \cdot q)$
does not mean the same as $-p \cdot -q$. In the first, or
weaker, expression, the *scope* of the negation includes the
entire expression within the parentheses. In the second, or
stronger, expression, each variable is negated separately.
It is clear that to say, "It is not true that I was both drinking
and driving," is not to say, "I was not drinking and I was
not driving."

3. Alternation $p \vee q$

This may be read "either p or q."

Either that's a ptarmigan or I've been grossly misled.

We have already seen that in logic, alternation is taken in a broad or inclusive sense. This usage was illustrated in the case of the major premise of an alternative syllogism. (See Chapter 5, p. 75.) In stating an alternation, we simply assert that at least one of the alternants is true and possibly both. In ordinary conversation the more common intention of "p or q" is "p or q and not both." We use this exclusive sense of "either . . . or . . . " when we say, "Either today is Monday or it's Tuesday." We have observed, however, that this disjunction is not symbolized by $p \lor q$ but by one of these two forms:

$$p \lor q \cdot -(p \cdot q)$$

or, simply:

$$p \land q$$

Both are read "Either p or q, and not both p and q." But we have seen too that even in ordinary discourse we sometimes use the broad or inclusive sense of "either . . . or . . . " Given that "Either the cat ran away or he's been hurt," it does not follow from the truth of the statement, "The cat ran away," that therefore the statement "The cat is not hurt" is false. With this in mind, the truth table for $p \lor q$ will be easy to construct.

Compact Form

p	q	$p \lor q$		p	$\lor$	q
T	T	T		T	T	T
F	T	T		F	T	T
T	F	T		T	T	F
F	F	F		F	F	F

The truth table for *disjunction* or exclusive alternation will be different:

Compact Form

p	q	$p \land q$		p	$\land$	q
T	T	F		T	F	T
F	T	T		F	T	T
T	F	T		T	T	F
F	F	F		F	F	F

The logical difference between alternation and disjunction may also be seen in forms known as *Boolean expansions*.[1] Under what conditions will $p \vee q$ be true? Under these three:

1. When p is true and q is false.
2. When both p and q are true.
3. When p is false and q is true.

Therefore $p \vee q$ is equivalent to the following:

$$(p \cdot -q) \vee (p \cdot q) \vee (-p \cdot q)$$

But the Boolean expansion of $p \vee q$ consists of an alternation of only two conjunctions:

$$(p \cdot -q) \vee (-p \cdot q)$$

4. Implication $p \supset q$

This may be read "p implies q" or "if p, then q." For the variables, we may substitute any values:

If you love me, then I shall be eternally happy.
If arsenic is heated, it sublimes.
If a wombat is tickled, it will laugh.

In formal logic we take implication in a broad or inclusive sense which is a little like the inclusive senses of conjunction and alternation, but rather more puzzling because it rarely occurs in ordinary conversation. In conventional discourse, we normally use what is called *strict implication*.

If West Germany is invaded, there will be war.

Here we intend that the antecedent p and the consequent q have some kind of causal connection with each other. However, even in ordinary conversation there are occasions when we seem to assert a noncausal relationship of implication between an antecedent and a consequent. In John Gay's *The Beggar's Opera*, Lucy Lockit is questioned by her father about her lover who has escaped from Newgate Prison. She says, "If I know anything of him, I wish I

[1] After George Boole, whose book, *An Investigation of the Laws of Thought* (8), is generally regarded as the immediate starting point of modern symbolic logic.

may be burnt." Lucy seems to be trying to convey the impression that the proposition "I know anything of him" is just as false as the proposition "I wish I may be burnt," and no causal connection exists between them. Yet she uses the phrase "if . . . then . . .". Other examples of this usage are:

> If the Soviet Union weakens, then shrimps will whistle.
> If she's 22, then I'm a monkey's uncle.
> Wal, I'll be a horned toad effen it ain't Alkali Pete.[2]

Implication, in this broad or inclusive sense, is called *material implication*. This is a somewhat misleading name, for it suggests connection with matters of fact in contrast to formal relations. This is not the case, for material implication is a purely formal relationship between p and q, a relationship so weak that we may say that any true proposition materially implies any other true proposition; any false proposition materially implies any proposition; and any true proposition is materially implied by any proposition. A statement of material implication is false only when its antecedent is true and its consequent false. "$p \supset q$" means that it is not the case that p is true and q is false. We are now ready to put down the truth table for $p \supset q$ in conventional short form:

p	$\supset$	q
T	T	T
F	T	T
T	F	F
F	T	F

5. Biconditional or Material Equivalence $p \equiv q$
We read this "p if and only if q."

> Paul is married if and only if he has a wife.

[2] Some logicians deny that such examples from ordinary language as "if he passed his exam, I'm a Dutchman (I'll eat my hat, etc.)" are instances of material implication. They are, says P. F. Strawson, "simply quirks, verbal flourishes, odd uses of 'if.' If hypothetical statements were material implications, the statements would not be a quirkish oddity, but a linguistic sobriety and a simple truth." *Introduction to Logical Theory* (45).

If "Paul is married" is true, then "he has a wife" is true. But if "Paul is married" is false, then "he has a wife" is false. In other words, when p is true, q is true (and conversely); and when p is false, q is false (and conversely). In sum, p and q *have the same truth value.* For when one is true, the other is true: and when one is false, the other is false. Thus the biconditional connective "≡" stands for a relation which logicians call *material equivalence.* Two propositions are said to be materially equivalent if p implies q and q implies p. That is, "p and q are materially equivalent" means the same as "if and only if p is true, then q is true." The truth table for the biconditional connective is as follows:

p	≡	q
T	T	T
F	F	T
T	F	F
F	T	F

INTERDEFINITIONS OF TRUTH FUNCTIONS

It is not necessary to define all truth functions by truth table. We can define some by truth table, others in terms of those already defined. Here we shall see how conjunction, alternation, and implication may be defined in terms of one another plus negation. The sign "=" may be read "means."

A. *Implication*

1. Implication can be defined in terms of conjunction and negation. This we have seen above in our explanation of material implication:

$$p \supset q = -(p \cdot -q)$$

2. Implication may also be defined in terms of alternation and negation:

$$p \supset q = -p \lor q$$

That is, "if p then q" means "either not p or q."

> "If she's engaged, she's lovely" means
> "Either she's not engaged or she's lovely."

"If Kurtz is beheaded, he's dead" means
"Either Kurtz is not beheaded or he's dead," etc.

B. *Alternation*

1. Alternation may be defined in terms of negation and conjunction:

$$p \lor q = -(-p \cdot -q)$$

The expression "$p \lor q$," as we know, means either p or q. That is, it cannot be the case that both are false. Hence "either p or q" may be said to mean "it is not the case that not-p and not-q."

> "Either Yeats wrote *The Windhover* or Hopkins did" means
> "It is not the case that neither Yeats wrote *The Windhover* nor Hopkins wrote *The Windhover*.

2. Alternation may also be defined in terms of implication and negation:

$$p \lor q = -p \supset q$$

If at least one of the alternants must be true, then if one of them is false, the other is true:

> "Either somebody talked or she suspects something" means
> "If somebody didn't talk, then she suspects something."

C. *Conjunction*

1. Conjunction may be defined in terms of negation and alternation:

$$p \cdot q = -(-p \lor -q)$$

That is, "p and q" may be defined as "it is not the case that either not-p or not-q."

> "Heaven is my home and my postal address is Kalamazoo, Michigan," means
> "It is not the case that either Heaven is not my home or my postal address is not Kalamazoo, Michigan."

2. Conjunction may also be defined in terms of negation and implication:

$$p \cdot q = -(p \supset -q)$$

"The baby has been pinched and it will cry" means
"It is not the case that if the baby has been pinched, it will not cry."

Here is a summary of interdefinitions above:

1. $p \supset q = -(p \cdot -q)$
2. $p \supset q = -p \lor q$
3. $p \lor q = -(-p \cdot -q)$
4. $p \lor q = -p \supset q$
5. $p \cdot q \;\; = -(-p \lor -q)$
6. $p \cdot q \;\; = -(p \supset -q)$

CHECKING INTERDEFINITIONS BY TRUTH TABLE

We may check the soundness of a definition by constructing truth tables for both of its parts and comparing the truth values. This method of checking is often called the *matrix method*. For example, suppose we check the definition above:

$$p \supset q = -p \lor q$$

First let us look at the right-hand expression, "$-p \lor q$." What are the elements in this expression? Starting from the simplest components and proceeding to the more complex, we note first of all that we have p and q. Then there is the negation of p, or $-p$. Finally, there is the expression as a whole, $-p \lor q$. Now let us fix on the simplest elements, and write out all possible combinations of the truth values of p and q thus:

p	q
T	T
F	T
T	F
F	F

Let us write out the possible combinations of the truth values when $-p$ is introduced. This is easy, for the values of $-p$ will be exactly the opposite of those for p.

p	q	$-p$
T	T	F
F	T	T
T	F	F
F	F	T

Consider now the total expression $-p \lor q$. Will it hold when p is true, q true, and $-p$ false? Yes, for the truth of q satisfies the requirements of the expression "either not-p or q." Take the second row. Will $-p \lor q$ hold when $-p$ is the case, when p is false and q is true? Yes, for the falsity of p satisfies the requirements of "either not-p or q." But in the third row, $-p \lor q$ cannot hold when $-p$ is false, p is true and q is false; in order to satisfy $-p \lor q$ we must have either p false or q true, and the third row of our truth table offers us neither of these cases. The fourth row, however, gives us truth values consistent with that of $-p \lor q$, for in this row $-p$ is the case. Let us write out the table for this part of our definition, first in expanded form:

p	q	$-p$	$-p \lor q$
T	T	F	T
F	T	T	T
T	F	F	F
F	F	T	T

Now let us arrange the table in the more compact and conventional way. This we do by writing the expression $-p \lor q$, then placing the truth values of p and q in columns immediately under those letter symbols. Then we place the truth values for $-p$ under the negation sign. Finally, we write down the values for the entire expression under the alternation sign, which in this case heads the main column in our truth table for $-p \lor q$:

$-$	p	$\lor$	q
F	T	T	T
T	F	T	T
F	T	F	F
T	F	T	F

Finally, let us recall the truth table for our left-hand expression, $p \supset q$. We remember from page 93 that this table in compact form reads:

p	$\supset$	q
T	T	T
F	T	T
T	F	F
F	T	F

Now we are ready to compare our findings. We discover that the truth values in the main column for the expression $-p \lor q$ are *exactly the same* as those in the main column for $p \supset q$. This confirms our definition:

$$p \supset q = -p \lor q$$

TESTING TAUTOLOGIES BY TRUTH TABLE

At this point we must introduce the idea of a *tautology*. In ordinary usage the word "tautology" is often employed to refer to any expression containing needless repetition of something. To "ascend up" and "to erase out" are sometimes called tautologies, although such expressions might better be called *redundancies* or *pleonasms*. Expressions in ordinary language which follow the form "A is A" are closer to the logical sense of tautology. But statements such as "A rose is a rose," and "Pigs is pigs," may not be tautological, even though they seem of the form "A is A." For in such statements there is usually an unexpressed shift of emphasis which makes the predicate term mean more than the subject. Thus, when a man says "Boys will be boys," he probably intends something like the following:

> x is a boy and it is to be expected
> that x will exhibit the characteristic
> properties of boys, such as trying to
> put frogs down little girls' necks.

But in formal logic, *tautology* has a strict but simple meaning, and it is to this we must attend. A tautology is an expression which is always true; it is necessarily true, true no matter what. More technically, it is a function the truth value of which as read from a truth table is always "true." An example of a tautology is:

$$p \lor -p$$

This is comparable to the "law of the excluded middle," one of the classical laws of logic. We may read it "either p or not-p." It is evident that this formula will be "true no matter what"; for if p is true the expression as a whole is true, and if p is false the entire expression is again true. Another law of classical logic is the principle of noncontradiction:

$$-(p \cdot -p)$$

This too is a tautology, for it holds whether p be true or false. The contradictory of a tautology is an expression which is *self-contradictory*, as:

$$p \cdot -p$$

Such expressions are *necessarily false*, for their truth values as read from a truth table will always be "false." Here are the truth tables for the tautologies referred to above; we note that the main columns in each case contain only T's:

p	$\vee$	$-p$
T	T	F
F	T	T

$-$	$(p$	$\cdot$	$-p)$
T	T	F	F
T	F	F	T

Suppose we are asked to determine whether or not the expression "$p \supset (p \vee q)$" is a tautology. How do we go about it? First we construct truth tables for q and for $p \vee q$, respectively:

q	$\supset$	$(p$	$\vee$	$q)$
T	T	T	T	T
T	F	T	T	T
F	T	T	T	F
F	F	F	F	F

Now compare the truth values for q, the antecedent, with those of the main column of $p \vee q$, the consequent. They are:

T	T
T	T
F	T
F	F

Finally, let us ask: Is there any row of the table in which the antecedent is true and the consequent false? No, there is not. But we know that a statement of the form $p \supset q$ is true in *every* case *except* that in which the antecedent is true and the consequent false (see above, p. 93, for the truth table for $p \supset q$). Hence our given expression $q \supset (p \lor q)$ is true for every assignment of truth values to p and q: there is no assignment of truth values under which q is true and $p \lor q$ is false.

q	$\supset$	$(p$	$\lor$	$q)$
T	T	T	T	T
T	T	F	T	T
F	T	T	T	F
F	T	F	F	F

The main column in the truth table for the entire expressions contains nothing but T's. We conclude that the given formula is a tautology.

On the other hand, the expression "$(p \lor p) \supset q$" is *not* a tautology, as a glance at its truth table will show:

$(p$	$\lor$	$p)$	$\supset$	q
T	T	T	T	T
F	F	F	T	T
T	T	T	F	F
F	F	F	T	F

There is one row (the third) of the table in which the antecedent $(p \lor p)$ is true and the consequent q is false. Thus a "false" appears in this row of the main column of the formula. But we know that the main column of a tautology's truth table contains only T's. Hence the given formula cannot be a tautology.

Is the formula $(p \supset q) \equiv (-p \lor q)$ a tautology? Let us construct and then examine its truth table:

p	$\supset$	q	$\equiv$	$-$	p	$\lor$	q
T	T	T	T	F	T	T	T
F	T	T	T	T	F	T	T
T	F	F	T	F	T	F	F
F	T	F	T	T	F	T	F

A glance at the truth table for *material equivalence* (see above, page 94) tells us that the truth values of the main columns of both the right- and the left-hand expressions satisfy the conditions for an equivalence; for two expressions are materially equivalent when they have the same truth value. This being the case, we write a T in each row under the sign of equivalence, "$\equiv$." This becomes the main column of the entire formula. Since the main column of the formula's truth table contains nothing but T's, the formula is shown to be a tautology.

Equivalences: the De Morgan Laws

We have just seen that the expression:

$$(p \supset q) \equiv (-p \lor q)$$

is a tautology. This means that not only is $p \supset q$ *materially equivalent* to $-p \lor q$ but also that they are *logically equivalent*. What is the distinction between material and logical equivalence? The statement "$p \equiv q$" may be read "p is materially equivalent to q." This statement is sometimes true and sometimes false: it is true whenever p and q are replaced by statements with the same truth value (for example, "London is in England" and "Paris is in France"); it is false whenever p and q are replaced by statements with different truth values (for example, "London is in England" and "Paris is in England"). Now since the statement "p is materially equivalent to q" is only *sometimes* true and not *always* true, p and q are not logically equivalent. In other words, *two statements* P *and* Q *are logically equivalent only when* P $\equiv$ Q *is a tautology* (that is, when "P is materially equivalent to Q" is always true.) Hence, having proved that:

$$(p \supset q) \equiv (-p \lor q)$$

is a tautology, we know that $p \supset q$ and $-p \lor q$ are logically equivalent.

There is a law of logic called the "law of double negation":

$$p \equiv -(-p)$$

The reader can quickly verify for himself that this law is a tautology by constructing its simple truth table. Since (1) the law states that p and $-(-p)$ are materially equivalent, and (2) its truth table shows the law to be a tautology, it follows that p and $-(-p)$ are logically equivalent, or, as we should now say, *equivalent*.

Let us test another statement of material equivalence to see whether or not it is a tautology:

$$p \cdot q \equiv -(-p \vee -q)$$

We begin with the right-hand expression "$-(-p \vee -q)$." Its elements are first p and q, then the negations of these, then the expression within the parentheses "$-p \vee -q$," and finally the total expression "$-(-p \vee -q)$." We write out the possible combinations of truth values for p and q, adding to these the combinations for $-p$ and $-q$, taking care to write the T's and F's in such order that all possible truth-value combinations for these elements will be covered.[3]

p	q	$-p$	$-q$
T	T	F	F
F	T	T	F
T	F	F	T
F	F	T	T

Next let us look at the expression within the parentheses, "$-p \vee -q$." Given the values in the matrix so far, in which of the four rows above will $-p \vee -q$ be true and in which false? The answer is that only in the first row will $-p \vee -q$ be false. For this expression to be true, at least one of the alternants p, q must be false. But the table's first row says that p and q are true, and that $-p$ and $-q$ are false. Thus the truth-values of the first row are inconsistent with $-p \vee -q$. Hence this expression's truth-value in the first row is F. Here, then, is the truth table for $-p \vee -q$, the main column appearing under the alternation sign:

$-$	p	$\vee$	$-$	q
F	T	F	F	T
T	F	T	F	T
F	T	T	T	F
T	F	T	T	F

[3] The values for p being written TFTF and for q TTFF, the values for $-p$ and $-q$ are simply negatives of those for p and q.

Now take the right-hand expression "$-(-p \lor -q)$" as a whole. We still have the negation outside the parentheses to deal with. But this is an easy matter, for *its* truth table will be exactly the *contradictory* of that of the expression *inside* the parentheses, "$-p \lor -q$." Thus we add another column to our truth table under the outside negation sign, and this becomes the main column for the expression "$-(-p \lor -q)$":

$-$	$(-$	p	$\lor$	$-$	$q)$
T	F	T	F	F	T
F	T	F	T	F	T
F	F	T	T	T	F
F	T	F	T	T	F

At this point we turn back to the left-hand expression in the original statement "$p \cdot q \equiv (-p \lor -q)$." We know that the truth table for $p \cdot q$ is:

p	$\cdot$	q
T	T	T
F	F	T
T	F	F
F	F	F

Now let us compare the truth values in the main column for $-(-p \lor -q)$ with those for the main column for $p \cdot q$. They are exactly the same.

$p \cdot q$	$-(-p \lor -q)$
T	T
F	F
F	F
F	F

Finally, we must ask: Is this statement of material equivalence "$p \cdot q \equiv (-p \lor -q)$" a tautology? The answer is yes. How do we know? Consider the first row of the tables compared just above, with the truth table of material equivalence (see above, page 94) in mind. If $p \cdot q$ is true and $-(-p \lor q)$ is true, is the statement that they are materially equivalent true or false? True. Is the statement of their material equivalence true or false when both are false?

True. But this gives us all "trues" in the main column (that under "≡") of the truth table of the statement as a whole; in its final form the table looks like this:

p	·	q	≡	−	(−	p	∨	−	q)
T	T	T	T	T	F T	F	F	F	T
F	F	T	T	F	T F	T	F	F	T
T	F	F	T	F	F T	T	T	T	F
F	F	F	T	F	T F	T	T	T	F

Since the given statement of the material equivalence is a tautology, $p \cdot q$ and $-(-p \vee -q)$ are equivalent. The reader will be relieved to learn that tautologies like the above, as well as more complicated ones, can be checked on a logic machine (truth-function evaluator) in a matter of seconds. (See Appendix, p. 210.)

Equivalent expressions may be obtained by transforming the contradictories of certain compound expressions according to laws known as the De Morgan laws, named for Augustus De Morgan (1806–1871), the English logician and mathematician. Here are two De Morgan laws:

1. The negation of a conjunction is equivalent to the alternation of the negated elements. (That is, conjunctive functions, when negated, yield alternative functions).

$$1. \; -(p \cdot q) \equiv (-p \vee -q)$$
$$2. \; -(p \cdot -q) \equiv (-p \vee q)$$
$$3. \; -(-p \cdot q) \equiv (p \vee -q)$$
$$4. \; -(-p \cdot -q) \equiv (p \vee q)$$

2. The negation of an alternation is equivalent to the conjunction of the negated elements. (That is, alternative expressions, when negated, yield conjunctive expressions.)

$$1. \; -(p \vee q) \equiv (-p \cdot -q)$$
$$2. \; -(-p \vee q) \equiv (p \cdot -q)$$
$$3. \; -(p \vee q) \equiv (-p \cdot q)$$
$$4. \; -(-p \vee -q) \equiv (p \cdot q)$$

The reader may verify for himself that the De Morgan formulae are equivalences.

TESTING ARGUMENTS BY TRUTH TABLE

The validity of many arguments constructed from truth-function connectives can be tested by truth tables.

An argument is a set of statements containing one or more premises and a conclusion. In a valid argument, the premises *logically imply* the conclusion. We have already met *material* implication ("⊃"). Now the difference between logical and material implication is parallel to the difference between logical and material equivalence. The statement "*p* ⊃ *q*" may be read "*p* materially implies *q*." This statement is sometimes true and sometimes false: it is false only when *p* is true, and *q* is false; it is true for all other assignments of truth-values to *p* and *q*. Now although the statement "*p* materially implies *q*" is *sometimes* true, we say that since it is not *always* true, *p* does not *logically imply q*. That is, *a statement* P *logically implies another statement* Q *only if the statement* "P *materially implies* Q" *is always true* (that is, only if P ⊃ Q is a tautology). If P logically implies Q, we can infer, deduce, conclude Q from P; if P logically implies Q, an argument from P to Q is valid.

It can now be seen how we may test the validity of an argument by truth tables. What are the specifications for the truth table of a valid argument from premises to conclusion? There is only one: *there must be no row in which the truth-values of the premises are all T and the conclusion F.* Take a simple conjunctive argument of the form "*p* and *q* are true; therefore *q* is true."

$$p \cdot q$$
$$\therefore q$$

Here is the truth table for the argument:

p	$p \cdot q$ (premise)	q (conclusion)
T	T	T
F	F	T
T	F	F
F	F	F

What are the specifications for the truth tables of a valid argument from premises to conclusion? There is only one: *There must be no case in which the truth value of the premises is T and that of the conclusion F.* The truth table above fulfills this condition; hence the argument is valid.

Now let us test the familiar implicative argument of *modus ponens* form:

$$p \supset q$$
$$p$$
$$\therefore q$$

Here is the truth table:

p (premise)	$p \supset q$ (premise)	q (conclusion)
T	T	T
F	T	T
T	F	F
F	T	F

Under no assignment of truth values do the premises come out true and the conclusion false. Hence the argument is valid.

Suppose we test the following argument:

$$p \supset q$$
$$-p$$
$$\therefore -q$$

In the truth table for this argument we must remember to make columns for $-p$ and $-q$ in addition to those for p and q.

p	q	$p \supset q$ (premise)	$-p$ (premise)	$-q$ (conclusion)
T	T	T	F	F
F	T	T	T	F
T	F	F	F	T
F	F	T	T	T

We notice that in the second row the truth value of the premises is T and that of the conclusion F. Hence the argument is invalid. It is, of course, the familiar fallacy of *denying the antecedent*.

The validity of alternative arguments may be tested in the same way. Two such arguments are given below together with their truth tables. The first is valid, the second invalid.

1. $p \lor q$
    $-p$
    $\therefore q$

p	q	$p \lor q$ (premise)	$-p$ (premise)	q (conclusion)
T	T	T	F	T
F	T	T	T	T
T	F	T	F	F
F	F	F	T	F

2. $p \lor q$

p

$\therefore -q$

p	q	$p \lor q$ (premise)	p (premise)	$-q$ (conclusion)
T	T	T	T	F
F	T	T	T	F
T	F	T	T	T
F	F	F	F	T

Finally, let us test the argument:

$$p \supset q$$
$$q \supset r$$
$$\therefore p \supset r$$

Since this argument involves three variables, the truth table will have eight rows so that all possible combinations of p, q, and r will be covered.

p	q	r	$p \supset q$ (premise)	$q \supset r$ (premise)	$p \supset r$ (conclusion)
T	T	T	T	T	T
T	T	F	T	F	F
T	F	T	F	T	T
T	F	F	F	T	F
F	T	T	T	T	T
F	T	F	T	F	T
F	F	T	T	T	T
F	F	F	T	T	T

There is no case in which the truth value of the premises is T and that of the conclusion F. Hence the argument is valid.

BIBLIOGRAPHICAL NOTE

Truth functions are explained in Basson and O'Connor (4), which is the most compact introduction to symbolic logic available at present. Ambrose and Lazerowitz (1) has an excellent account of truth functions. There are good directions for constructing truth tables in Johnstone (26) and Cooley (12).

QUESTIONS AND EXERCISES

1. Put the following into symbolic notation:
    1. Personnel should be promoted if and only if they are fully qualified.
    2. Either Bacon or Marlowe wrote Shakespeare's plays, but not both.
    3. Either the child is admitted to school immediately or he is sent home and notified of his admission.
    4. If that kangaroo is awarded a medal, he will either cry or jump for joy.
    5. It is not true that either a green light or a yellow light permits a motorist to proceed.
    6. If either Alissa did not wear her amethyst pin or Jerome didn't leave, and Jerome did not leave; then Alissa did not wear her amethyst pin.
    7. Receiving either a grade of D or F implies that the student has neither done satisfactory work in this course nor qualified himself for the next advanced course.
    8. If I have ever been in love (and I think that I have), I have never been in love with anyone but you.—T. S. ELIOT.
    9. Unless you read music, you cannot have the job.
    10. Only if the moon is full do great auks dance.
    11. If you don't talk to Marian, she won't talk to you.
    12. If driving a car implies having a license, then driving a horse or a car implies driving a horse or having a license.

2. Make up subject matter for the following forms:

    1. $-(-p \cdot q)$
    2. $[(r \supset s) \cdot (s \supset r)] \supset (s \equiv r)$
    3. $[(p \supset q) \cdot p] \supset q$
    4. $-[-p \lor (q \lor r)]$
    5. $[p \supset (q \lor r)] \supset s$
    6. $[(p \lor q) \cdot -q] \supset p$
    7. $[p \lor (q \lor r)] \supset (s \lor t)$
    8. $[(p \cdot q) \cdot p] \supset q$
    9. $-p \cdot -q$
    10. $-(p \cdot q)$

11. $-(-p \cdot -q)$

12. $p \supset [(q \vee r) \vee (s \vee t)]$

3. Arrange the following in three series of equivalent expressions:

1. $(p \supset q)$
2. $(p \vee q)$
3. $(p \cdot -q)$
4. $-(-p \vee q)$
5. $-(-p \cdot -q)$
6. $(-q \supset -p)$
7. $-(p \supset q)$
8. $-(p \cdot -q)$
9. $(-p \supset q)$
10. $(-p \vee q)$

4. Test the following arguments by truth table:
1. p is true; therefore p or q is true.
2. p and q are true; therefore p is true.
3. either p or q is true, and q is true; therefore p is false.
4. either p or q or r is true, and p and q are true; therefore r is true.
5. p implies q and q is true; therefore p is true.
6. p implies q and q is false; therefore p is true.

5. Give Boolean expansions of the following expressions:

1. $p \vee -q$
2. $-p \vee q$
3. $p \vee q$
4. $-p \vee -q$
5. $p \vee q \vee r$
6. $p \vee -q \vee r$

6. Construct examples from ordinary discourse which illustrate each of the following functions:
1. Biconditional
2. Disjunction
3. Alternation
4. Implication
5. Conjunction
6. Equivalence
7. Negation

7. What is a tautology? Can a tautology give us any new factual information?

8. Determine by truth tables which of the following formulae are tautologies.

a. $(p \cdot q) \supset p$

b. $(p \vee p) \supset p$

c. $(p \vee q) \equiv (p \cdot q)$

d. $(p \supset q) \supset (-p \vee q)$

e. $(p \cdot q) \supset (p \vee q)$

     f. $(p \lor q) \supset p$

     g. $(p \lor q) \equiv -(p \cdot q)$

9. Are the following equivalent? Give reasons.
   1. It is not the case that if his fingerprints are on file with the FBI, he's a criminal.
   2. It is not the case that either his fingerprints are not on file with the FBI or he's a criminal.
   3. His fingerprints are on file with the FBI and he is not a criminal.

10. Prove by truth tables that the De Morgan Laws below are tautologies:

    1. $-(p \lor q) \equiv (-p \cdot -q)$ 5. $-(p \lor -q) \equiv (-p \cdot q)$
    2. $-(p \cdot q) \equiv (-p \lor -q)$ 6. $-(-p \cdot q) \equiv (p \lor -q)$
    3. $-(-p \lor q) \equiv (p \cdot -q)$ 7. $-(-p \lor -q) \equiv (p \cdot q)$
    4. $-(p \cdot -q) \equiv (-p \lor q)$ 8. $-(-p \cdot -q) \equiv (p \lor q)$

11. Fill in the following truth table.

p	q	$p \cdot q$	$-(p \cdot q)$	$-p \cdot -q$	$p \lor q$	$-p \lor -q$	$p \supset q$
T	T						
F	T						
T	F						
F	F						

7

How Deductive Systems Are Constructed

The Axiomatic Method

The ancient Greeks invented a method which has always been regarded as the firmest basis for systems of formal concepts. This method, familiar to anyone who has studied geometry, consists in taking a set of general statements (called *axioms* or *postulates*) as true, and drawing from these ("deducing") a series of further statements called *theorems*. Showing that these theorems do follow from the axioms or from previously established theorems is called "demonstration" or "proof."

Until quite modern times it was thought that the axiomatic method was limited to geometry. But in our time the whole of mathematics has been subjected to this method. For example, the Italian mathematician G. Peano (1858–1932) showed how the whole of arithmetic can be organized as a deductive system. In this system, all the statements of arithmetic derive from only five simple postulates, plus certain rules and definitions. Of course arithmetic is not usually presented to school boys and girls in strictly axiomatic fashion, for that would require proving such statements as $2 + 2 = 4$ as theorems. To do this, the teacher would have to show that the truth of this arithmetical statement follows deductively from a whole battery of prior theorems, these in turn deriving from a set of unproved postulates. This would be rather difficult for boys and girls to follow.

With the appearance of *Principia Mathematica* by Whitehead and Russell (*47*) in 1910, the borders of formal science were widened in a remarkable way. Mathematics was claimed to be but an extension of logic. The authors of the *Principia* pointed out that mathematics presupposes the ideas of logic. Since then, to our own day, great numbers of logical systems have been constructed in axiomatic form. The development of this technique of logical construction has greatly extended our knowledge of formal conceptual schemes, and has thrown remarkable light on the foundations of mathematics.

Elements of a Deductive System

A formal deductive system may be said to consist of the following elements:

1. A set of primitive symbols undefined within the system.
2. A set of rules which define what it is for an expression to be a "well-formed formula" of the system. These are called *formation rules;* they are syntax rules or rules of logical grammar.
3. A set of axioms or postulates none of which are proved within the system.
4. A set of *transformation* rules. It is these rules which enable us to derive theorems from the axioms.
5. A set of theorems.

The nature of these elements will be illustrated below in connection with two deductive systems.

Deductive systems may be compared to young peoples' construction sets of the Erector or Meccano variety. These construction sets come boxed with all the basic material—metal strips, wheels, nuts and bolts, and so forth. Included in the set is an instruction booklet which tells how to make various models out of the material provided. The first model illustrated is usually some very simple thing like a gate, made from two or three pieces. More complex models follow, until finally directions are given to make elaborate cranes, windmills, and bridges. These complex models include principles of construction contained in the simpler devices. Now the basic material of the set—wheels, strips, bolts, etc.—correspond to the basic notions and unproved axioms of the system. Just as there are directions which tell the proper ways to put the construction pieces together, so axiomatic systems contain rules by means of which postulates may be transformed into theorems. The completed bridges, towers, cranes, and trucks correspond to the proved theorems of the deductive system. The formation rules would, so to speak, be built into the pieces themselves—you cannot put a wheel on a nut; they won't go together.

We shall now look at simplified and informally presented versions of two well-known types of deductive systems developed in modern formal logic: the *calculus of propositions* and the *calculus of classes*. The propositional calculus might be considered as a broad extension of ideas we first met with in connection with the conditional syllogism; the class calculus, on the other hand, is more closely related to the categorical syllogism.

THE CALCULUS OF PROPOSITIONS

The calculus of propositions or *propositional calculus* is a deductive system which can be constructed from truth-functional connectives of the kind we examined in the preceding chapter. In our exposition of this calculus, it is first necessary to say something about the symbols used in the system, its postulates, and its rules.

1. Primitive Symbols

These include the propositional variables p, q, r, etc. With these we are familiar. These also include the following two connectives:

Negation   —
Alternation $\lor$

These are undefined within the system. The only steps we can take with them are steps which are explicitly permitted by the rules and axioms. The connective for *implication* ($\supset$) is not a primitive symbol. It is introduced by a definition:

Definition 1. $p \supset q = -p \lor q$

Other definitions will be introduced as needed. The "=" sign is not a primitive symbol of our system. It will appear only within definitions, not in postulates or theorems. Definitions will tell us that the expression to the left of this sign is identical with the expression to the right and may replace it whenever it occurs.

2. Rules of Formation

Formation rules are necessary in a deductive system so that the statements used in the system will be meaningful and not nonsensical. The expressions $p \lor q$ *and* $-(-p \lor -q)$ are meaningful, but the expressions $\lor r \supset$ and $- \lor p \equiv$ are obviously silly. In the present system, each variable (p, q, etc.) is a "well-formed formula" (WFF), and the syntactical rules permit us to combine the symbols to form other WFF's. If any expression, say p, is a WFF, then $-p$ is a WFF. If any expressions, say p and q, are WFF's then $p \lor q$ is a WFF.

The scope of a connective is indicated symbolically by whatever method of punctuation we choose to employ. We shall use parentheses and square brackets. Note that in the expression $-(p \lor q)$ the scope of the negation extends to the entire expression inside the parentheses.

3. Postulates

Ideally, the postulates (axioms) of any deductive system should meet three conditions. First, they should be *consistent*. The postulates should not contradict one another, nor should contradictory theorems be deducible from them. Second, postulates of any deductive system should be *complete*. Just as a baseball umpire's rulebook should provide him with a basis for every decision he makes, so from the postulates of a deductive system we should be able to deduce every logically true statement which can be made in terms of the elements of the system. Third, postulates should be *independent* of one another. That is, we should not be able to deduce one from the other; for this means that we have more postulates than we need. But this third requirement is generally considered the least important. It is sometimes awkward to construct a deductive system in terms of the absolute minimum number of postulates. In their exposition of the truth-function calculus in the *Principia*, Whitehead and Russell used five postulates; later it turned out that one was provable from the others, so that only four were strictly necessary.

The sample theorems of our system are based on these four postulates set forth by Whitehead and Russell:

1. $(p \lor p) \supset p$ The Principle of Tautology (Taut.)
   If either p or p, then p.
   If either kangaroos are good-tempered or kangaroos are good-tempered, then kangaroos are good-tempered.

2. $q \supset (p \lor q)$ The Principle of Addition (Add.)
   If q, then p or q.
   If Martinis are cocktails, then either chipmunks eat worms or Martinis are cocktails.

3. $(p \lor q) \supset (q \lor p)$ The Principle of Permutation (Perm.)
   If either p or q, then either q or p.
   If either today is Wednesday or today is Thursday, then either today is Thursday or today is Wednesday.

4. $(q \supset r) \supset [(p \lor q) \supset (p \lor r)]$
         The Principle of Summation (Sum.)
   If q implies r, then p or q implies p or r.
   If being a man implies being rational, then being either a dodo or a man implies being either a dodo or rational.

We should note that the "$\supset$" sign which appears in the postulates was introduced into the system by definition, and is not a primitive. The postulates are written in this form (using the "$\supset$" sign) for ease of understanding; they could all, however, be rewritten without the implication sign. For example, $(p \lor p) \supset p$ could be rewritten $-(p \lor p) \lor p$.

4. Transformation Rules

Transformation rules for the deduction of theorems include (A) *the substitution rule* and (B) *the rule of inference* (or detachment).

A. *Substitution Rules.* There are two kinds of substitutions we may use to prove our theorems. One is substitution on variables and the other is definitional substitution.

Substitution on Variables. For any variable, p, q, r, etc., any variable or construct of variables in terms of the system (WFF) may be substituted in any postulate or theorem.

For example, take postulate Add.:

$$q \supset (p \vee q)$$

Let us substitute $-q$ for q. Such substitution is noted:

$$-q/q$$

Let us make a further substitution, replacing p by $-r \supset s$:

$$-r \supset s/p$$

We thus obtain a variation of the postulate of addition, and a theorem in the system:

$$-q \supset [(-r \supset s) \vee -q]$$

It is important to distinguish between the following substitutions:

$$-p/p \qquad p/-p$$

The first, in which $-p$ replaces p, is legitimate. The second is not, for the present rule permits only substitution on variables. We can, however, replace the variable p in the expression $-p$ by q to obtain $-q$.

We should note that substitution on variables must be carried out *completely*. That is, if we are substituting $-p$ for p, we must make this substitution on each and every occurrence of p. When interpreted, statements within our deductive system will be *tautologies*, that is, statements whose truth value is "true" no matter what statements are substituted for their variables. But if our substitution on variables is incomplete, we destroy the tautologous character of the statement on which the substitution is being performed. For example, suppose we substituted $-q$ for p in the principle of Tautology this way:

$$(-q \vee -q) \supset p$$

This would not be correct, for the substitution has been carried out only partially. The result is not a tautology, as a truth-table test would quickly show. We should have substituted $-q$ for every occurrence of p, thus:

$$(-q \vee -q) \supset -q$$

Definitional Substitution. For any expression, any other expression definitionally identical with it may be substituted in any postulate or proved theorem.

For example, take the expression:

$$(p \supset q) \supset [(p \supset q) \vee (r \supset s)]$$

By Definition 1, we may make the following substitution:

$$-p \vee q / p \supset q$$

to obtain:

$$(-p \vee q) \supset [(-p \vee q) \vee (r \supset s)]$$

Unlike substitution on variables, definitional substitution need not be carried out completely. The substitution above could have been carried out in the following way:

$$(-p \vee q) \supset [(p \supset q) \vee (r \supset s)]$$

B. *The Rule of Inference* (Inf.). This rule, sometimes called the rule of detachment, authorizes an operation familiar to us as the principle of the implicative syllogism, *modus ponens:*

$$\frac{\begin{array}{c} p \supset q \\ p \end{array}}{q}$$

That is, if *p* is true, and *p* implies *q*, then we may validly infer the truth of *q*. Or, in the present system, if *P* is a postulate or proved theorem, and *P* implies *Q*, then we may infer *Q*.

5. Theorems[1]

I. $q \supset (p \supset q)$

> Dem.
>
> | 1. $q \supset (p \vee q)$ | Add. |
> |---|---|
> | 2. $q \supset (-p \vee q)$ | 1. $-p/p$ |
> | 3. $q \supset (p \supset q)$ | 2. Def. 1 |

Our theorem states "If *q*, then *p* implies *q*," thus asserting one of the so-called "paradoxes of material implication"—a

[1] This is a sample set only. The complete set of theorems for the elementary logic of propositions is found in Whitehead and Russell (*47*), Vol. 1, pp. 98 *et seq.*

true proposition is implied by any proposition. The first step in our demonstration is to take the postulate Add.:

$$q \supset (p \vee q)$$

and by the rule of substitution on variables substitute $-p$ for p. This gives us:

$$q \supset (-p \vee q)$$

Now by Definition 1 ($p \supset q = -p \vee q$,) we may simply replace $-p \vee q$ by its definitional equivalent $p \supset q$. This gives us our theorem:

$$q \supset (p \supset q)$$

II. $(p \supset -p) \supset -p$

> Dem.
>
> | | |
> |---|---|
> | 1. $(p \vee p) \supset p$ | Taut. |
> | 2. $(-p \vee -p) \supset -p$ | 1. $-p/p$ |
> | 3. $(p \supset -p) \supset -p$ | 2. Def. 1 |

This theorem, the proof of the principle of *reductio ad absurdum*, shows that a proposition which implies a contradiction (in this case its own falsity) is false.

In this demonstration, it may not be immediately apparent why we are able to replace $-p \vee -p$ by $p \supset -p$. Speaking very informally, this is simply a variation on the substitution of identities by Definition 1. We know by this definition that $-p \vee q = p \supset q$. If we make a substitution of $-p$ for q in this definition, we get $-p \vee -p = p \supset -p$. In general, an alternation may be changed into an implication by dropping (or adding) one negation sign from (to) the left-hand alternant, replacing the alternation sign by the implication sign, and leaving the right-hand alternant unchanged.

III. $(p \supset -q) \supset (q \supset -p)$

> Dem.
>
> | | |
> |---|---|
> | 1. $(p \vee q) \supset (q \vee p)$ | Perm. |
> | 2. $(-p \vee -q) \supset (-q \vee -p)$ | 1. $-p/p, -q/q$ |
> | 3. $(p \supset -q) \supset (q \supset -p)$ | 2. Def. 1 |

IV. $(q \supset r) \supset [(p \supset q) \supset (p \supset r)]$

> Dem.
>
> | | |
> |---|---|
> | 1. $(q \supset r) \supset [(p \vee q) \supset (p \vee r)]$ | Sum. |
> | 2. $(q \supset r) \supset [(-p \vee q) \supset (-p \vee r)]$ | 1. $-p/p$ |
> | 3. $(q \supset r) \supset [(p \supset q) \supset (p \supset r)]$ | 2. Def. 1 |

V. $p \supset (p \lor p)$

> Dem.
>
> 1. $q \supset (p \lor q)$ Add.
> 2. $p \supset (p \lor p)$ 1. p/q

To demonstrate our next theorem we must use the rule of inference (Inf.), which permits us to conclude that Q is true if P implies Q, and P is true.

VI. $p \supset p$

Dem.

1. $(q \supset r) \supset [(p \supset q) \supset (p \supset r)]$ IV
2. $[(p \lor p) \supset p] \supset [(p \supset (p \lor p)) \supset (p \supset p)]$ 1. $(p \lor p)/q, p/r$
3. $(p \lor p) \supset p$ Taut.
4. $[p \supset (p \lor p)] \supset (p \supset p)$ 2, 3, Inf.
5. $p \supset (p \lor p)$ V
6. $p \supset p$ 4, 5, Inf.

Theorem VI is related to the classical law of identity. ("If a proposition is true, it is true," or "Whatever is, is.") This law, together with the law of noncontradiction, $-(p \cdot -p)$, and the law of the excluded middle, $p \lor -p$, constitute the three "laws of thought" of classical logic. It is interesting to note that here a *postulate* of classical logic is proved as a *theorem*. (The "IV" and "V" in the first and fifth steps of the proof refer, of course, to the fourth and fifth theorems.)

VII. $-p \lor p$

The reader may supply the proof.

VIII. $p \lor -p$

> Dem.
>
> 1. $(p \lor q) \supset (q \lor p)$ Perm.
> 2. $(-p \lor p) \supset (p \lor -p)$ 1. $-p/p, p/q$
> 3. $-p \lor p$ VII
> 4. $p \lor -p$ 2, 3, Inf.

This is the principle of the excluded middle, the second of the classical "laws of logic" we have proved as a theorem.

IX. $p \supset -(-p)$

The reader may supply the proof.

The connectives "$\cdot$" (conjunction) and "$\equiv$" (equivalence) are introduced by the following definitions:

Definition 2. $p \cdot q = -(-p \lor -q)$
Definition 3. $p \equiv q = (p \supset q) \cdot (q \supset p)$

The next theorem uses Definition 3. Although the two types of rules we have given above would be sufficient to construct the propositional calculus, for the sake of simplicity in proving theorems, a third transformation rule will be introduced at this point. It is called the rule of conjunction (Conj.) and is stated: *The conjunction of any two true statements is also true.* That is, if P and Q are postulates or proved theorems, then their conjunction $P \cdot Q$ is a theorem.

X. $(p \lor p) \equiv p$
    Dem.
    1. $(p \lor p) \supset p$ Taut.
    2. $p \supset (p \lor p)$ V
    3. $[(p \lor p) \supset p] \cdot [p \supset (p \lor p)]$ 1, 2, Conj.
    4. $(p \lor p) \equiv p$ 3, Def. 3

To clarify this proof, think of $(p \lor p)$ as p, and p as q. Then apply Definition 3.

Further theorems in the sentential calculus include the following, which—with the exception of the last—are stated without proof. For demonstrations of these and other theorems, the reader may consult any of the texts listed at the end of the chapter.

XI. $-(-p) \supset p$
XII. $-(-p) \equiv p$

Theorem XII states the principle of double negation; the denial of $-p$ is equivalent to p.

XIII. $(p \supset q) \supset (-q \supset -p)$
XIV. $(-p \lor -q) \supset -(p \cdot q)$

The reader will recognize the relation of theorem XIV to one of the De Morgan laws.

XV. $-(p \cdot -p)$
    Dem.
    1. $p \lor -p$ VIII
    2. $[-p \lor -(-p)]$ 1. $-p/p$
    3. $(-p \lor -q) \supset -(p \cdot q)$ XIV
    4. $[-p \lor -(-p)] \supset -(p \cdot -p)$ 3, $-p/q$
    5. $-(p \cdot -p)$ 4, 2, Inf.

Theorem XV is the "law of noncontradiction," the best known of the three classical laws of logic.

THE CALCULUS OF CLASSES

What is a class? We seem to know this intuitively; there is the class of cats, of Europeans, of pretty girls, and so on. But it is not easy to put down in words just what we mean by the term "class." Are classes *things*, parts of the "ultimate furniture of the world"? Or are they simply convenient *fictions*, logical constructs only? Happily, it is not our task to discuss this difficult question.

Classical logicians pointed out that every general name, such as "cat" or "chair," can be taken in two ways. First, there is the *connotation* or *intension* of the term—that is, the sum of its attributes or properties, the answer to the question "What is it?" But there is also the *denotation* or *extension* of the term—the individuals to which the term applies. Thus, the connotation of "chair" is "separate seat for one," while its denotation is this chair, that chair, *every* chair. Historically, the development of logic in the West may be traced in terms of this distinction. For logicians in the British-American tradition generally have concerned themselves with the denotative side of names—their extension. While Continental philosophers, on the other hand, have traditionally been more interested in the connotative aspect of names—the intension of terms. Hence philosophers on the Continent have tended to develop the more metaphysical logic of *concepts*. While the logic of concepts resulted in remarkable systems of general philosophy like that of Hegel (whose conception of logic was metaphysical), concentration on the extensional logic of classes was of much more direct value to the development of modern axiomatic systems of mathematics and logic.

As we have seen, the categorical syllogism lends itself very easily to analysis in terms of class relationships. But it was not until George Boole published his *An Investigation of the Laws of Thought* in 1854 that it became possible to construct a general logic of classes which would include the syllogism, but also go far beyond its boundaries.

Boole perceived and acted on the possibility of developing a logic of classes in a way analogous to algebra. That is, instead of taking the a's, b's, and c's of ordinary algebra as *quantities*, he took them as *classes*. Thus what came to be called "mathematical logic" came into being. Boole's work was further developed by a number of logicians and mathematicians, particularly the German E. Schröder and the American C. S. Peirce. Boole's algebra is not limited to a calculus of classes, for a calculus of propositions can be constructed out of it. But historically the development of the sentential calculus came a little later than Boole's algebra, rising from the work of G. Frege and G. Peano, whose investigations into the problem of the foundations of mathematics were published toward the end of the last century. The *Principia Mathematica* of Whitehead and Russell assimilated and extended both of these early lines of development of modern generalized logic.

Basic Notions: Class Sums and Products; 0 and 1

Our description of the calculus of classes or *"Boolean algebra"* will be brief and informal. We shall take the idea of *class* as an undefined notion. The symbols a, b, c, and so forth are variables ranging over classes. Classes may be *combined* in two ways, somewhat analogous to arithmetical addition and multiplication, to yield class *sums* or class *products*. Class sums and class products are themselves classes. The class sum is symbolized:

$$a + b$$

If a stands for men and b for women, then $a + b$ stands for the class that includes both men and women. The class product is noted

$$a \times b$$

If a stands for voters and b for taxpayers, then $a \times b$ stands for the class containing the common members, the voters who are taxpayers. The difference between a class sum and a class product may vividly be illustrated by the reader himself if he will in imagination summon to his yard first the actual members of the *product* of the classes "cat" and "musician," dismiss them, and then summon members of the *sum* of these same classes. The first assemblage will be rather small at best, but the second will overflow the reader's yard and hamper traffic in several adjoining communities.

We must now introduce the notions of two extraordinary classes, the *universal class*, symbolized by the numeral 1, and the *null class*, symbolized by 0. The universal class is the class to which *everything* belongs; the null class is the class to which *nothing* belongs. It is uninhabited, having no members. We have already encountered the notion of the null class as well as that of a class product in our earlier analysis of propositions by means of Venn diagrams. In that context, the class product was symbolized *ab* rather than $a \times b$. Thus, in the null forms associated with the Venn diagrams the statement "No pelicans are clergymen" was represented:

$$ab = 0$$

We shall here, however, use the longer form

$$a \times b = 0$$

The class calculus also employs another notion familiar to us from our earlier work with the Venn diagrams; this is the notion of the *negative* of a class. The negative of the class "cat" is the class "non-cat"; of "Baptist," "non-Baptist"; and so on. Everything that is not a cat is a member of the class "non-cat"; everything that is not a Baptist is a member of the class "non-Baptist," etc. Thus the Venn diagram symbolism for the classical A proposition "All basset hounds are patriots" is:

$$a \times \bar{b} = 0$$

That is, the product or common members of the classes "basset hound" and "nonpatriot" is the null class—the class of no members. Similarly, the I proposition, "Some ostriches are not members of the PTA," is rendered in Venn symbolism:

$$a \times \bar{b} \neq 0$$

The product of the classes "ostrich" and "nonmember of the PTA" is *not* an uninhabited class; it has at least one member.

The Venn diagram below illustrates these class notions:

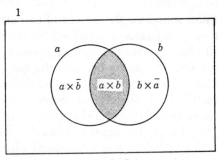

$$a \times b = 0$$

The rectangle, taken as a whole, stands for the universal class 1. a and b are classes and their common area $a \times b$ is the class product. In this case, since the area $a \times b$ is shaded, we know that the class product has no members. Areas $a \times \bar{b}$ and $b \times \bar{a}$ involve class negation: the first is available for habitation by a's that are non-b's; the second provides for b's that are non-a's.

One other notion is needed in the class calculus; it is that of *class identity*. It is symbolized by the sign $=$. If a stands for mammals and b for warm-blooded vertebrates, then

$$a = b$$

Postulates

Following E. V. Huntington, the postulates of the class calculus are generally set forth in pairs.

1a. If a and b are classes, $a + b$ is a class.
1b. If a and b are classes, $a \times b$ is a class.

The first pair of postulates establishes class sums and products as themselves classes.

2a. There is a class 0 such that $a + 0 = a$, for any class a.
2b. There is a class 1 such that $a \times 1 = a$, for any class a.

The class which is the *sum* of the class "cats" and the null class is the same as the class "cats." The class which is the *product* of the class "cats" and the universal class is the same as the class "cats." Or, in metaphysical language, cats that are *beings* are all cats.

3a. If a and b are classes, $a + b = b + a$.
3b. If a and b are classes, $a \times b = b \times a$.

The first postulate is the commutative law for class sums (class addition); the second is the commutative law for class products (class multiplication). The obvious analogy is to arithmetic, where:

$$7 + 5 = 5 + 7$$
and
$$7 \times 5 = 5 \times 7$$

4a. If a, b, and c are classes, $a + (b \times c) = (a + b) \times (a + c)$.
4b. If a, b, and c are classes, $a \times (b + c) = (a \times b) + (a \times c)$.

These are the distributive laws for class sums and products. The second has an analogue in arithmetic; the first does not.

5a. For any class a there is a class $\bar{a}$ such that $a + \bar{a} = 1$.
5b. For any class a there is a class $\bar{a}$ such that $a \times \bar{a} = 0$.

That is, if we add giraffes to nongiraffes we get the universe; but there are no members of the combined class "giraffes that are nongiraffes."

6. There are at least two classes a and b such that a is not identical with b. ($a \neq b$)

Neither a cosmos in which there was only one kind of thing nor a calculus which had only one class would be very interesting.

Definitions

A most important idea of Boolean algebra is that of class inclusion:

$$a \subset b$$

This is read "a is included in b." Although the symbol $\subset$ may be new to us, the notion of class inclusion is familiar, for we used it constantly in our work on the classical syllogism. Indeed, it is in the theory and calculus of classes that we see most clearly the connection between modern deductive logic and the traditional logic of the syllogism. If we were to set forth a complete class calculus, we would soon discover that the syllogism is but a particular case of the logic of classes. For example, consider:

If $a \subset b$, and $b \subset c$, then $a \subset c$.

This is the equivalent of the classical *dictum de omni et nullo,* which states: what is true of a whole class is true of its parts (subclasses or members of the class).

There are many definitions of class inclusion, but for the purpose of our sample theorems only two need be introduced:

Definition 1. $(a \subset b)$ may be written $(a \times \bar{b} = 0)$
Definition 2. $(a \subset b)$ may be written $(a \times b = a)$

Rules for the Deduction of Theorems

The rules for class calculus are analogous to the rules for the sentential calculus.

1. *Rule of Substitution on Class Variables.* For any variable $a, b, c,$ any variable or construct of variables designating a class may be substituted in any postulate or proved theorem. Substitution on variables must be carried out completely.

For example, substituting $\bar{a}$ for b and 0 for c in postulate 4b, we obtain:

$$a \times (\bar{a} + 0) = (a \times \bar{a}) + (a \times 0)$$

2. *Rules governing use of class identity* $(=)$:

A. Identity Substitution (Id.S.). Identical classes may be substituted for each other. For example, postulate 5a gives us authority to substitute $a + \bar{a}$ for 1 in postulate 2b to obtain:

$$a \times (a + \bar{a}) = a$$

B. Transitivity of Identity (Id.T.). This rule also tells us that classes identical with the same class are identical with each other. For instance, if

$$a = (a + a) \times 1$$

and

$$(a + a) \times 1 = a + a$$

then

$$a = a + a$$

C. Commutation of Identity (Id.C.). This rule permits commutation of identities, so that $a = a + a$, for example, may be changed to $a + a = a$.

Rules corresponding to the principles of inference and conjunction in sentential calculus are used in the logic of classes. A separate rule based on the principle of *reductio ad absurdum* is necessary for the proofs of certain theorems. This rule may be stated: *Whatever leads to a contradiction is false.*

SAMPLE THEOREMS

For convenience, the postulates are given here in abridged form:

1a. $a + b$ is a class
1b. $a \times b$ is a class

2a. $a + 0 = a$
2b. $a \times 1 = a$

3a. $a + b = b + a$
3b. $a \times b = b \times a$

4a. $a + (b \times c) = (a + b) \times (a + c)$
4b. $a \times (b + c) = (a \times b) + (a \times c)$

5a. $a + \bar{a} = 1$
5b. $a \times \bar{a} = 0$

6. There are at least two classes a and b such that $a \neq b$

I. *There is at most one universal class 1 such that* $a \times 1 = a$.

This theorem does not state that $a \times 1 = a$, for this is assumed in postulate 2b. What the theorem does state is the *uniqueness* of the universal class. The proof makes use of the rule of *reductio ad absurdum*. That is, we assume what we are to prove is *not* so, and show that this assumption leads to its contradictory.

Proof:

1. Suppose there are two universal classes 1_a and 1_b such that
   $1_a \neq 1_b$. Then
      (i) $a \times 1_a = a$ **2b.**
      (ii) $a \times 1_b = a$ **2b.**
2. (i) $1_b \times 1_a = 1_b$ 1 (i), $1_b/a$.
     (ii) $1_a \times 1_b = 1_a$ 1 (ii), $1_a/a$.
3. $a \times b = b \times a$ **3b.**
4. $1_b \times 1_a = 1_a \times 1_b$ 3, $1_b/a$, $1_a/b$.
5. $1_b = 1_b \times 1_a$ By Commutation on 2 (i). (This will be written "2(i), Id.C.")
6. $1_b = 1_a \times 1_b$ From 5 and 4 by Transitivity of Identity. (This will be written "5, 4, Id.T.")
7. $1_b = 1_a$ 6, 2 (ii), Id.T.
8. There is at most one universal class 1 such that $a \times 1 = a$.   The assumption that 1_a and 1_b are distinct leads to a consequence which contradicts it.

II. *There is at most one null class 0 such that* $a + 0 = a$.
This proof is similar to that of Theorem 2 and may be worked out by the reader. Assume that there are two null classes 0_1 and 0_2 such that $a + 0_1 = a$, and $a + 0_2 = a$, and so on.

III. $a \times a = a$

Here is a theorem that looks notationally as if it would be scandalous in algebra, but is quite at home in the logic of classes. The class of "cats that are cats" is identical with the class "cats." When ordinary language is substituted in this way in basic theorems, the result seems so ridiculously obvious that one may well wonder why it is necessary to go to the trouble of demonstrating what everybody knows intuitively to be true. The answer to this objection is, of course, that the object of a logical calculus is not to demonstrate material common in everyday discourse, but rather to build a formal system, one of the properties of which is *rigor;* that is, a system in which nothing is assumed in a demonstration which has not previously been postulated or proved.

Proof:

1. $a \times (a + \bar{a})$	$= a$	Substituting $a + \bar{a}$ for 1 in **2b** by Id.S., given **5a**. (This will be written "**2b**, $a + \bar{a}/1$ Id.S. (**5a**)."
2. $a \times (a + \bar{a})$	$= (a \times a) + (a \times \bar{a})$	**4b**, a/b, $\bar{a}/c$.
3. $(a \times a) + (a \times \bar{a}) = a$		Commute 2, then 3 follows from this and 1 by Id.T.
4. $(a \times a) + 0$	$= a$	3, Id.S. (**5b**).
5. $(a \times a) + 0$	$= a \times a$	**2a**, $a \times a/a$.
6.	$a \times a = a$	Commute 5, then 6 follows from this and 4 by Id.T.

IV. $a + a = a$

If you add the class "Martians" to the class "Martians," you get "Martians." Proof of this theorem is much the same as that of Theorem 3. Begin by substituting $a \times \bar{a}$ for 0 in 2a.

V. $a = a$

Pigs are pigs. The reader can supply the very simple proof of this theorem which is related to the "Law of Identity" of classical logic. The analogous theorem in the propositional calculus is $p \supset p$.

VI. $a \times 0 = 0$

There are no archbishops that are members of the null class.

Proof:

1. $a \times 0$	$= (a \times 0) + 0$	**2a**, $a \times 0/a$, and commute.
2. $(a \times 0) + 0 = 0 + (a \times 0)$		**3a**; $a \times 0/a$, $0/b$.
3. $a \times 0$	$= 0 + (a \times 0)$	1, 2, Id.T.
4. $a \times 0$	$= (a \times \bar{a}) + (a \times 0)$	3, Id.S. (**5b**). Note that the substitution is made only on the first 0 on right-hand side.
5. $a \times (\bar{a} + 0) = (a \times \bar{a}) + (a \times 0)$		**4b**; $\bar{a}/b$, $0/c$.

6. $a \times 0$ $= a \times (\bar{a} + 0)$ Commute 5, then 6 follows from this and 4 by Id.T.

7. $\bar{a} + 0$ $= \bar{a}$ 2a; $\bar{a}/a$.

8. $a \times 0$ $= a \times \bar{a}$ 6, Id.S. (7).

9. $a \times 0$ $= 0$ 8, Id.S. (5b).

VII. $a + 1 = 1$

The class of all who are Elks or who belong to the universal class is identical with the universal class. Proof of this theorem is like that of Theorem VI. Substitute $a + 1$ for a in 2b to get

$$a + 1 = (a + 1) \times 1, \text{etc.}$$

VIII. $1 \neq 0$

Nothing is the negative of everything. The proof uses the principle of *reductio ad absurdum*.
Proof:

1. Suppose the contradictory: $1 = 0$. Then

   (i) $a \neq 1$ and   From 6, given $1 = 0$.

   (ii) $a \neq 0$

2. $a + 0 = a + 0$ V, $a + 0/a$.

3. $a + 1 = a + 0$ 2, Id.S. (1).

4. $a + 1 = 1$ VII.

5. $a + 0 = a$ 2a.

6. $a + 0 = 1$ Commute 3, then 7 follows from this and 4 by Id.T.

7. $a = 1$ Commute 5, then 8 follows from this and 6 by Id.T.

8. $1 \neq 0$ The assumption that $1 = 0$ leads to a contradiction (7 and 1 (i)).

IX. $a \neq \bar{a}$

This is analogous to the law of double negation. Compare theorem XII in the propositional calculus. Gnus are not nongnus.
Proof:

1. Suppose $a = \bar{a}$

2. $a \times a = 0$ 5b, Id.S. (1)

3. $a = 0$ 2, Id.S. (III)

4. $a + a = 1$ 5a, Id.S. (1)

5.	$a + a = a$	IV
6.	$a = 1$	Commute 5, then 6 follows from this and 4 by Id.T.
7.	$1 = 0$	Commute 6, then 7 follows from this and 3 by Id.T.
8.	$1 \neq 0$	VIII
9.	$a \neq \bar{a}$	The assumption that $a = \bar{a}$ leads to a contradiction (7 and 8).

In the class calculus, there are a number of theorems which involve the familiar notion of class inclusion. We remember that the symbol $\subset$ is read "is included in," and our two definitions of class inclusion:

Definition 1. $a \subset b$ means $a \times \bar{b} = 0$
Definition 2. $a \subset b$ means $a \times b = a$

The symbols $\supset$, $\cdot$, and $\equiv$ are familiar to us from our study of the propositional calculus. In the class calculus they may appear as connectives between any *statements* in the class calculus, their use being governed by the appropriate rules of the propositional calculus. They may *not* appear between symbols for classes.

X. $a \subset a$

This theorem, which asserts that any class is included in itself, follows from 5b and Definition 1.

XI. $(a \subset b) \cdot (b \subset a) \equiv a = b$

a is included in b, and b is included in a, if and only if a and b are identical. The technique of proof consists in showing that the consequent follows from the antecedent and vice versa. The analogue of this theorem in sentential calculus appears as the definition:

$$(p \equiv q) = [(p \supset q) \cdot (q \supset p)]$$

Proof:

1. Suppose
   (i) $a \subset b$
   (ii) $b \subset a$
   Then $(a \subset b) \cdot (b \subset a)$ 1(i), 1(ii); Conj.
2. (i) $a \times b = a$ 1 (i), Def. 2.
   (ii) $b \times a = b$ 1(ii), Def. 2.
3. $a \times b \quad = b \times a$ **3b**

4.	$a \times b \quad = b$	3, 2(ii), Id.T.
5.	$a = b$	Commute 2(i), then 5 follows from this and 4 by Id.T.

(This is the first half of the proof.)

6.	Suppose $a = b$	
7.	$a \times a = a$	III.
8.	$a \times b = a$	7, Id.S. (6).
9.	$a \subset b$	8, Def. 2.
10.	$b \times a = b$	7, Id.S. (6).
11.	$b \subset a$	10, Def. 2.
12.	$(a \subset b) \cdot (b \subset a)$	9, 11; Conj.

(This is the concluding half of the proof.)

XII. $0 \subset a$

The null class is included in every class. Analogously, in the propositional calculus, a false proposition implies any proposition.

Proof:

1.	$a \times 0 = 0$	VI.
2.	$\bar{a} \times 0 = 0$	1, $\bar{a}/a$.
3.	$\bar{a} \times 0 = 0 \times \bar{a}$	**3b**, $\bar{a}/a, o/b$
4.	$0 \times \bar{a} = 0$	Commute 3, then 4 follows from this and 2 by Id.T.
5.	$0 \subset a$	4, Def. 1.

XIII. $a \subset 1$

This theorem, which asserts that the universal class contains all classes, follows from 2b and Definition 2.

XIV. $0 \subset 1$

This is a corollary of Theorem XIII.

XV. $(a \subset \bar{a}) \supset (a = 0)$

The reader can easily supply the proof. The analogue of this theorem in the propositional calculus is:

$$(p \supset -p) \supset -p$$

For demonstration of further theorems in class calculus, the reader may consult the reference works listed below.

BIBLIOGRAPHICAL NOTE

Useful expositions of the propositional calculus may be found in Eaton (*19*), pp. 362 *et seq.*; Ambrose and Lazerowitz (*1*), Chap. 8. The class calculus is explained in Eaton, pp. 419

et seq.; Ambrose and Lazerowitz, Chap. 12; Churchman (*10*) Chap. 12; and Langer (*29*), Chap. 9.

QUESTIONS AND EXERCISES

1. Prove the following exercises theorems in propositional calculus.

A. $p \supset (q \vee p)$	Use Add.
B. $-p \vee p$	Use Theorem VI and Def. 1.
C. $p \supset -(-p)$	Use Theorem VIII and Def. 1.
D. $(p \supset q) \supset (-q \supset -p)$	Use Perm and Def. 1.
E. $(-q \supset -p) \supset (p \supset q)$	Proof similar to D.
F. $(p \supset q) \equiv (-q \supset -p)$	Use E, F, and Def. 3.
G. $(-p \vee -q) \vee (p \cdot q)$	Use Theorem VIII and Def. 2.
H. $q \supset (-p \supset q)$	
I. $(-p \supset -q) \supset (q \supset p)$	
J. $(-p \supset q) \supset (-q \supset p)$	

2. Given the following as axioms, prove the stated theorems. (Assume rules permitting substitution on variables and of equivalences; assume also the rule of Inference.)

I. $p \supset q \equiv -p \vee q$ theorem	A. $(-q \supset -p) \supset (p \supset q)$
II. $p \cdot q \equiv -(-p \vee -q)$	B. $(-p \supset q) \supset (-q \supset p)$
III. $(p \vee q) \supset (q \vee p)$	C. $(-p \vee -q) \vee (p \cdot q)$
IV. $(p \supset -q) \supset (q \supset -p)$	D. $-p \vee p$
V. $-(-p) \equiv p$	E. $p \supset p$
VI. $p \vee -p$	F. $-(p \supset q) \equiv p \cdot -q$

3. This was one of Lewis Carroll's "pillow problems." A barber shop has three barbers, A, B, and C. (1) A is infirm, so if he leaves the shop B has to go with him. (2) All three cannot leave together, since then their shop would be empty. Now with these two premises, let us make an assumption and test its consequences. Let us assume that C goes out. Then it follows that if A goes out, B stays in (by premise 2). But (by premise 1) if A goes out, B goes out too. Thus our assumption that C goes out seems to lead to a conclusion we know to be false. If so, the assumption is false, and C cannot go out. But this is nonsense, for C obviously can go out without disobeying either of these restrictions. C can in fact go out whenever A stays in. Thus, strict reasoning from apparently consistent premises seems to lead to two mutually contradictory conclusions.

The problem is easily solved by propositional calculus. Let "A" stand for 'A goes out,' "B" for 'B goes out,' "C" for 'C goes out.' Premise 1 will then be $-(A \cdot -B)$, and premise (2) $-(A \cdot B \cdot C)$, etc.

4. What conditions should a set of postulates satisfy?

5. What is meant by *connotation?* By *denotation?* Choose three or four class names, and give the connotation and denotation of each. Do proper names have connotation? Denotation?

6. Give the justification for each step in the following proof of Theorem III in the class calculus:

1. $a \times 1 = a$
2. $a \times (a + \bar{a}) = a$
3. $a \times (b + c) = (a \times b) + (a \times c)$
4. $a \times (a + \bar{a}) = (a \times a) + (a \times \bar{a})$
5. $(a \times a) + (a \times \bar{a}) = a \times (a + \bar{a})$
6. $(a \times a) + (a \times \bar{a}) = a$
7. $(a \times a) + 0 = a$
8. $a + 0 = a$
9. $(a \times a) + 0 = a \times a$
10. $a \times a = (a \times a) + 0$
11. $a \times a = a$

7. Give the justification for each step in the following proof of Theorem VI in the class calculus:

1. $a + 0 = a$
2. $a = a + 0$
3. $a \times 0 = (a \times 0) + 0$
4. $a + b = b + a$
5. $(a \times 0) + 0 = 0 + (a \times 0)$
6. $a \times 0 = 0 + (a \times 0)$
7. $a \times 0 = (a \times \bar{a}) + (a \times 0)$
8. $a \times (b + c) = (a \times b) + (a \times c)$
9. $a \times (\bar{a} + 0) = (a \times \bar{a}) + (a \times 0)$
10. $(a \times \bar{a}) + (a \times 0) = a \times (\bar{a} + 0)$
11. $a \times 0 = a \times (\bar{a} + 0)$
12. $\bar{a} + 0 = \bar{a}$
13. $a \times 0 = a \times \bar{a}$
14. $a \times \bar{a} = 0$
15. $a \times 0 = 0$

8. Prove the following theorems in class calculus.

    1. The null class is unique   (Theorem II).

    2. $a + a = a$ (Theorem IV).

    3. $a = a$ (Theorem V).

    4. $a + 1 = 1$ (Theorem VII).

    5. $0 \subset \bar{a}$

    6. $a \subset a$ (Theorem X). Use Def. 2.

    7. $(a \subset \bar{a}) \supset (a = 0)$ (Theorem XV).

    8. $0 \subset 1$

    9. $a = (a \times b) + (a \times \bar{b})$ **Use 2b, 5a, and 4b.**

9. Given the following as axioms, prove the stated theorems. (Assume the rules permitting substitution on variables and those governing class identities.)

    I. $a = a + a$

   II. $a \times \bar{a} = 0$

  III. $a + b = b + a$

  IV. $a \subset b \equiv (a \times \bar{b}) = 0$

   V. $a + \bar{a} = 1$

  VI. $a \times 1 = a$

 VII. $a \times (b + c) = (a \times b) + (a \times c)$

        theorem 1 $a = a$

        theorem 2 $a \subset a$

        theorem 3 $a = (a \times b) + (a \times \bar{b})$

8

The Nature of Logical Truth

The rapid development of modern formal logic has cast up many puzzling questions concerning the foundations of logic itself. One of these puzzles concerns the nature of logical truth. In what sense, if any, can we say that the statements of logic are "true"? We use the word "true" in various ways. Sometimes we apply it to objects. "That is true gold," we say, or "He is a true friend." Here "true" means that the properties of the object conform to certain standards or values. More often, we use the word "true" (and its antonym "false") to apply to *statements*. The statement "John Adams was the second President of the United States" is true and so is "$2 + 2 = 4$," while the statement "Sinclair Lewis wrote *War and Peace*" is false. Now unlike natural objects, such as gold pieces or friends, statements are *linguistic* entities; they belong to the order of language and symbols rather than to the order of natural objects and events. That is why we hear it frequently said that *truth is a property of sentences*.

What is it that makes a true statement true? A statement is true if there is a situation such as it designates and false if no such situation exists. "It is raining" is true if it is raining, and false if it isn't raining. Many statements we use in everyday discourse, such as "That's a Canadian dime," refer to factual situations which are directly observable. It is relatively easy to understand not only what is meant by calling such statements true but also how we check or "prove" their truth. The statement "There is a mouse in that wastebasket" is true if there is such a fact, and it is not a difficult matter to check the truth of the statement by examining the wastebasket. There are, however, large classes of statements about objects not directly observable (atoms, for instance) and here the means of checking the truth of statements is not so simple. The objects dealt with by nuclear physics are far more abstract than those we observe as we clean house. Still, statements about anti-protons, as well as statements about mice, describe the world around us; it is, ultimately, by an appeal to fact that they are verified or falsified.

What about the truth of the statements of formal science—those of mathematics and logic? They talk about things which do not seem to be either directly observable, such as rain or mice, or indirectly observable, such as protons. Let us take the simple arithmetical statement often cited by public speakers as an example of an obvious and in-controvertible truth—"2 + 2 = 4." What makes it true? The statement does not seem to describe anything in the external world, because we never seem to find any numbers, *pure* numbers, in this world. Yet some, like John Stuart Mill, have believed mathematical statements to be very general descriptions of the properties of natural objects. This "realist" view of the propositions of mathematics has not been popular in our century.

Could we say that "2 + 2 = 4" is true because this statement *fits in,* or coheres with, the whole ordered scheme of ideas and statements we call "arithmetic"? In that case, "2 + 2 = 5" is false because it is out of joint with this formal scheme. That is (we remember that it is possible to set forth arithmetic in the form of an axiomatic system), we could say that "2 + 2 = 4" is true in that it is a theorem of arithmetic which follows from certain previously dem-onstrated theorems, these in turn following from certain axioms which are unproved but assumed to be true.

The same considerations hold for logical statements. The statements of formal logic are true in that they follow as theorems either from previously proved theorems or from the postulates or basic ideas of the particular logical system. Thus, "$(p \supset -p) \supset -p$" is true because it can be shown to follow from the postulate of tautology by means of the application of the transformation rules of the sen-tential calculus. But this seems only to push the question

back one step. From what source do the postulates and
rules of such formal systems derive their truth? Indeed, is
it proper to speak of such abstract statements and stipulations as being "true" at all?

We know that if we are given the statements "*p*" and
also "*p* implies *q*," we may validly infer by the rule of inference that therefore *q* is true. But from what foundation
does the rule of inference derive its authority? Is it arbitrarily set up like the rules of a card game? Is it true by
definition? Or is it true because it is a "law of thought,"
the human mind being so constituted that it *must think
that way*? Or is the word "true" simply not applicable to
such a case? The puzzle involved here may come into
sharper focus if we consider the question of the status of a
familiar logical postulate, the law of noncontradiction.

The Law of Noncontradiction

The principle of noncontradiction (a thing cannot
at once be and not be; a statement cannot be true and
false at the same time) is the most important of the three
basic axioms or "laws of thought" of classical logic. Leibniz
considered it the foundation of mathematics. The Scholastics held that it was not only a logical but a metaphysical truth. Aristotle put it at the base of all science. In
modern logical systems the law of noncontradiction does
not always appear as a postulate (in our sentential calculus it is proved as a theorem); yet it may be used as a
postulate in a modern system. Moreover, in many systems
where the law is not used explicitly, some analogue of the
law does stand in the list of axioms. So it is quite proper
for us to take the law of noncontradiction as a typical example of a logical law, as we inquire into what it means
to say (if we may say so at all) that such laws are *true*.

Aristotle considered the law of noncontradiction self-
evidently true. Says he: "There is a principle in things
about which we cannot be deceived, but must always, on
the contrary, recognize the truth. It is that the same thing
cannot at one and the same time be and not be. . . . The
same attribute cannot belong and not belong to the same

subject and in the same respect."[1] Suppose we supply Aristotle with examples. A door cannot be open and shut at the same time, and a shoe cannot be black and white in the same place. A dog cannot bark and not bark at once. Now is the law of noncontradiction anything more than a rule stating that a sentence cannot be both true and false? According to Aristotle and the classical logicians who followed him, the principle of noncontradiction is indeed a basic rule of discourse in both logic and language. But, they claimed, it is more than this. The law is fundamentally a very general *description* of how things behave in nature *outside* the realm of logic and language, as well as inside it. Whatever is, says Aristotle, whether it be in the realm of human discourse or in the totality of Nature, obeys this all-pervasive law. The law of noncontradiction, Leibniz adds, holds good for everything, not only for things in this world but for *all possible worlds*. Thus, to the classical logicians, the principle of noncontradiction is a fundamental law to which conform not only *sentences* but also *natural objects and events*.

Logical Laws as Analytic Statements

At first sight, the law of noncontradiction does appear to be what the classical logicians claimed—a very wide and inclusive generalized description of the characters of things. Dogs certainly don't bark and not bark at the same time, and it is impossible for a galaxy to revolve and not revolve "in the same respect." In fact, it is difficult to think of *any* natural object or event in this or in any other world which does *not* "obey" this law. But many recent logicians flatly deny that the law of noncontradiction is anything more than a *rule of language*, a rule which happens to be useful both in formal logic and in ordinary discourse. These logicians (let us call them *"formalists"*) insist that the law of noncontradiction cannot be a general statement about the behavior of things in Nature, for *it is not a descriptive statement*. It is an *analytic* statement or *tautology*. An analytic statement is one which is true by definition,

[1] Aristotle, *Metaphysics* (2), Book IV, 1061[b] 34, 1005[b] 18.

such as "A bachelor is an unmarried man." Such statements admit of no exceptions, not because they describe invariable properties of Nature, but rather because they are based on an agreement as to how we are going to use language. If we met a man who said that he had just met a bachelor who was *not* an unmarried man, we would not say to him, "What an interesting exception to the general law—something like an albino crow!" Rather we would reply, "You are not using the word 'bachelor' the way everybody else uses it. You must mean a 'bachelor of arts' or some other thing like that." Analytic statements are not *falsifiable;* no event could happen that would make them untrue.

In contrast to analytic statements, a *synthetic* or *descriptive* statement is *not* true by definition. Rather it is true because it squares with some set of facts outside the order of language. Descriptive statements may be singular, such as "This kitten is healthy" and "Eisenhower is President," or *general,* such as "The sun always rises" and "The specific gravity of gold is 19.3." In either case, descriptive sentences point beyond language to factual situations. They are not simply stipulations as to how we should use words, or rules for putting sentences together. Unlike analytic statements, synthetic (descriptive) statements *are* falsifiable. Events can happen that would make them false; the facts they point to could be otherwise. The kitten *may* fall ill; the sun *could* explode.

Now, according to the formalist, the propositions of formal science (this includes logic and mathematics) are not synthetic but analytic. They are true by definition. They are tautologies—expressions whose truth value is always true, expressions which could not but be true. Consider the law of the excluded middle. (A thing must either be or not be; a statement must be either true or false.) Is is not obvious that this holds whether p is true or false? So too with the law of noncontradiction. This law is true simply by virtue of its formal structure, not because it describes any physical, metaphysical, or moral state of affairs. Because of its close relation to the rules of ordinary discourse, we are apt to be partial to the law of noncontradiction and to grant it privileged status. But the principle of tautology:

$$(p \lor p) \supset p$$

is just as much a logic axiom as the law of noncontradiction; yet it would never occur to anyone to claim that the principle of tautology describes some all-pervasive quality of Nature. To say, "If today is Tuesday or today is Tuesday, then today is Tuesday," should be more than enough to convince one that such formulae can tell us nothing at all about natural events. The purpose of the axioms of formal logic is to serve as frames within which we can arrange formal systems of abstract relations, not as descriptions of matters of fact. As Wittgenstein said, "I know nothing about the weather when I know that it rains or does not rain."

There is another point the formalist may suggest to strengthen his claim that the statements of logic and mathematics are true only "by definition." Ordinary mathematical and logical systems seem to have their own subject matter. The statements of such systems appear to be *about* certain ideas peculiar to the system. Statements of arithmetic seem to be about numbers. Statements of Euclidean geometry appear to concern spatial relations and can easily be translated into statements about physical space. Propositions of conventional logical calculi seem to be about sentences, classes, or similar logical entities. But these appearances, says the formalist, are deceptive. Statements constituting logical systems are not "about" any subject matter in particular. A "pure" logic would be the study of structures of formal implication without regard to their applicability to such specific ideas as sentences and classes. A "pure" geometry would make no assertions about such familiar things as lines and points on the surface of the earth, no statements about physical space.

All this leads up to the rather eerie suggestion that the systems of formal relations which underlie ordinary logic and mathematics *are not about anything at all*. A pure logic and a pure mathematics would consist of a system of signs which would remain meaningless until interpreted onto some kind of subject matter such as the distances between the stars. That is why Bertrand Russell said that in mathematics we do not know what we are talking about or whether what we are saying is true.

Why is it, they ask, that natural objects and events *seem* to obey the law of noncontradiction? The planet Uranus cannot move around the sun and in the same respect remain motionless. Nor can the trumpeter play his horn and at the same time not play it. The reason we think that natural objects and events follow the law of noncontradiction, says the formalist, is that we confuse the order of language and symbols with the order of Nature. This is a very old confusion, responsible in the past, so we are told, for many philosophers' errors. All natural language has certain fundamental rules, more comprehensive than those of grammar. Such a rule is the law of noncontradiction. It is a very natural error to mistake a characteristic or peculiarity of *language* for a property of the *world*—since we cannot talk or perhaps even think about that world save in language. Thus, the error of the *logical realists* (so the formalist might call Aristotle and all who consider the law to be a genuine description of natural objects and events) is a sophisticated variation of the naïveté of the peasant who avowed that the pig is rightly so called because it is a very dirty animal. In sum, the formalist position is that the law of noncontradiction is no more than a basic syntactical rule, a rule of putting sentences together in such a way as to ensure sensible communication. It should not be confused with a scientific law which endeavors to describe some regularity or pattern of behavior in Nature.

Objection to the Formalist Position

Nature neither "obeys" nor "disobeys" the law of noncontradiction. Nature just *is*. It is logic and language alone that obey and must obey this law. Ordinary discourse is based on the two truth values "true" and "false," and it is an unspecified but basic stipulation of ordinary discourse that our communication with one another should adhere to this rule. For if in talking to one another we do *not* abide by the principle of noncontradiction, we will talk *nonsense*.

But if the law of noncontradiction is no more than a basic rule of language, may we not ask why it is *this* rule and not another that is used in logic and common discourse? Is the choice of such a fundamental rule a matter of convention only? Is the law arbitrarily chosen; would some other law do just as well? In the past, formalists have said yes to this question; the choice of the law of noncontradiction as a fundamental rule for logic and language is no more and no less than a matter of convention. Today, however, this answer is generally considered too simple. The formalist is more likely to say that the law of noncontradiction is indeed a rule of language and not a description of how things behave in Nature, but the preëminence of this law is not the result of convention or of arbitrary choice. A logic based on the law of noncontradiction is simply *more useful* to our purposes than one which is not. A language having the principle of noncontradiction at its roots is better equipped to handle the general situation with which language is called upon to deal. The choice between a system containing a law of noncontradiction and some other system has an objective basis—the greater degree of adequacy as a tool for ordering and communicating knowledge.

But the logical realist may reply to this pragmatic view with the claim that the very introduction of the notion of *utility* of the law of noncontradiction weakens the case for any formalist interpretation of the law. Does not the fact that a system based on the principle of noncontradiction is more useful than one which is not strongly suggest that the world itself exhibits patterns which reflect the law? A key that is useful in opening a lock is one whose cut conforms in some way with the inner structure of the lock. Restricting the application of the law to the realm of language only drives the distinction between the linguistic and the natural orders too far and too hard. The realist admits that there is truly a difference between the order of language and the order of Nature. But in certain important ways language can, and does, reflect the structure of the world itself, even though this reflection is approximate and partial. For example, the distinction between nouns, verbs, and adjectives in many natural languages mirrors the distinction between things, events, and qualities in Nature.

Is the Analytic-Synthetic Distinction Absolute?

Another, and more recent, objection to the formalist position is this: To say that the law of noncontradiction, in contrast to statements about matters of fact, is simply a linguistic rule or purely analytic statement is to assume that there is an absolute difference between *analytic* and *synthetic* (descriptive, empirical) statements. But is it really that case that a gulf lies between the two classes of statements? Perhaps the formalist, in his enthusiasm over the success of the formalization of logic and mathematics in axiomatic systems, has driven the distinction between analytic and factual statements too far. According to W. V. Quine, human knowledge is an ordered whole, a conceptual scheme; only at its periphery does this system of concepts touch sense experience. The scheme of concepts we call science is a manifold of interconnected propositions, ranging from statements about observable objects like fruit flies or quartz crystals to statements about atomic events such as the spins of electrons. Toward the center of this system are the laws of logic and mathematics. These are statements which we would be very reluctant to modify or give up, for such modification or surrender would require drastic revision of the whole scheme—a scheme which works well for us, since it enables us to control natural forces and to predict future events. Nowhere in the scheme of science, however, can we find a fundamental break between two types of statements such as that presupposed by the formalist distinction between analytic (formal) statements and synthetic (factual) statements. It is just because the laws of logic and mathematics are at the core of our conceptual scheme that we consider them unshakeable, i.e., necessarily true. But even the laws of logic and mathematics should not be regarded as *in principle* immune to revision. (Already there has been talk of revising the law of the excluded middle as a means of simplifying quantum mechanics.) Hence there should be no *absolute* distinction between analytic and synthetic statements. Formalist doctrines which assign to the statements of logic and mathematics a kind of truth utterly different from the general descriptions of physical science rest on a dichotomy too extreme to stand without qualification.

Limitations of Axiomatic Systems; Gödel's Proof

The statements of mathematics and logic are analytical, true by virtue of their consistency with all the other propositions of the particular systems of which they are a part, these propositions following as theorems from sets of postulates taken as true by convention or arbitrary choice.

Such an oversimple "postulationalist" doctrine on the nature of logical truth can no longer be put forward without serious modification. Spurred on by brilliant successes in casting logic and mathematics into axiomatic systems, twentieth-century formal scientists hoped to show that the truth of all propositions of any and every logical or mathematical system could be formally and finally proved by demonstrating the *completeness* of the system. But it is now known that such proof is impossible. In 1931, the mathematician Kurt Gödel (1906—) demonstrated that for certain formal systems, such as ordinary arithmetic, there will always be true propositions expressible in terms of those systems which cannot be proved from the axioms. Such propositions are "formally undecidable" and the systems in which they appear are "incomplete."

What is the significance of Gödel's proof? It seems to point to an inherent limitation in the axiomatic method, once thought to be absolute as a means of demonstrating the truth of statements of formal science. It shows that the older formalist theories of the foundations of logic or mathematics are no longer tenable without important quali-

fications. In the words of a recent popular appraisal of
Gödel's work, "Gödel's proof means that the resources of
the human intellect have not been, and cannot be, fully
formalized, and that new principles of demonstration for-
ever await invention and discovery."[2]

The Paradoxes of Logic

Prior to Gödel's proof, there were many earlier in-
dications that the formalist theory of logic and mathematics
was overly simplified. Among such symptoms were the appearance of *paradoxes* in logical systems. A logical paradox
or "antinomy," as it is sometimes called, is a self-contradictory concept or statement, one that violates the law of noncontradiction, or implies such a violation. If we should
discover that upon the assumption of S (a statement) it
necessarily follows that therefore "not-S" *and* that if "not-S,"
then S, we have hit upon a logical paradox.[3]

A famous antinomy is "Russell's Paradox," discovered
by Bertrand Russell (1872—), coauthor with A. N.
Whitehead of the *Principia Mathematica* (47). This is
the paradox of the class of all classes that are not
members of themselves. All classes, it would seem, may
be divided into two kinds: those that do not contain themselves as members and those that do. An example of the
first is the class "cat." The class of all cats is not itself a
cat. An example of the second is the class of all conceivable
notions, since this class is itself a conceivable notion. Let
us call the first kind of class nonself-inclusive and the
second type self-inclusive. Let NSI stand for the class of
all nonself-inclusive classes. The question is: Is NSI a
nonself-inclusive class? If it is nonself-inclusive, it is a
member of itself. But if it is a member of itself, it is
self-inclusive, hence if it is nonself-inclusive it is self-
inclusive. Yet if on the other hand NSI is self-inclusive and
thus a member of itself, it must be nonself-inclusive, since

---

[2] Nagel and Newman, "Gödel's Proof" (*36*).

[3] Originally, a paradox meant any opinion not generally held, hence
any eccentric doctrine. This sense of "paradox" is assumed by De
Morgan in his book *A Budget of Paradoxes* (*14*), to which the reader
is referred for his enjoyment.

by definition all the members of NSI are nonself-inclusive; thus if it is self-inclusive, it is nonself-inclusive.

Intuitively familiar notions such as "class" often seem to us to need no further definition before we introduce them as elements of a deductive system. But the appearance of paradoxes like Russell's is evidence that such ideas, apparently crystal clear, frequently need careful formulation and restriction if we are to hope for a deductive system free of self-contradictory statements. Russell resolved the paradox by appeal to his "theory of types." The contradiction, he pointed out, is generated by failure to distinguish between things of different logical types. A class and its members are of different logical types. A class can have as members only things of a type lower than itself. Thus there can be no class which contains as members classes which are self-inclusive, for there are none. If this restriction is obeyed the paradox above cannot be generated.

Another type of paradox that has interested modern logicians is the ancient antinomy of Epimenides the Cretan, who said:

All Cretans are liars.

Let us assume that by "liar" is meant one whose statements are invariably false. Let us also assume that all other Cretan statements are in fact lies. Then the following situation arises. If Epimenides is telling the truth, then his statement is false, for he is a Cretan. But if his statement is false, there must be at least one true statement made by a Cretan. Since we have assumed that all other Cretan statements are false, the exception can only be the statement just made. Hence if Epimenides' statement is false, he speaks the truth. The statement of Epimenides is technically not the best formulation of the "antinomy of the liar," for in terms of Epimenides' assertion the antinomy is defective. A more precise form of the Cretan paradox is:

The statement in the rectangle on this page is false.

The paradox results from allowing statements to refer to themselves. It is eliminated if we distinguish sharply between *levels of language*. In the *object*-language we talk about things, as for example, the statement "Lucia is unfaithful." In the *meta*-language we talk about statements, as in this case "The statement 'Lucia is unfaithful' was made by Mario." And so we move progressively up through the various levels of statements. If we keep these levels clearly distinct, we can see that no statement can refer to itself, and thus the paradox is eliminated.

When the ancient Skeptics said, "No knowledge is certain," their critics triumphantly pounced on the apparent self-contradiction. By this very statement of doctrine, said they, the Skeptic implicitly claims certainty for at least one piece of knowledge, his own doctrine. But could not the Skeptic escape the charge of self-contradiction by insisting that no statement should be taken as referring to itself? Such a debate actually occurred in philosophical circles in our own time when the English positivist A. J. Ayer announced his support of the doctrine that only analytic and factual-descriptive propositions are meaningful, all others, including metaphysical propositions such as "God is the cause of the world" being nonsensical.[4] Antipositivist critics quickly wanted to know about *that* proposition, "Only analytic and descriptive propositions are meaningful." It is not an analytic statement, such as "2 + 2 = 4"; for if it were, everyone who understood it would agree with it, which is not the case. And it is obvious that it is not a proposition describing a matter of fact, such as "It is raining." Being neither analytic nor factual then, said the critics, one can only conclude that the proposition "Only analytic and descriptive propositions are meaningful" is nonsense. Ayer's defenders were not slow to invoke Russell's theory of types, pointing out that the statement "Only analytic and descriptive propositions are meaningful" should not be taken as self-referring. Replied the antipositivists, "That's a dodge!"

[4] Ayer, *Language, Truth and Logic* (3), p. 213.

BIBLIOGRAPHICAL NOTE

For a discussion of the meaning of "truth" as applied to mathematical propositions, see Hempel's essays, "On the Nature of Mathematical Truth" and "Geometry and Empirical Science" (23). The first of these essays contains an account of Peano's axiom system as a basis for arithmetic as well as a defense of the view that propositions of formal systems are true "by definition." Aristotle's account of the law of noncontradiction is in Book IV of his *Metaphysics* (2). Nagel surveys the problem of the principle of noncontradiction in his essay, "Logic Without Ontology" (35), and suggests a solution of the pragmatic type. For Quine's attack on the absolute distinction between analytic and descriptive propositions, see his "Two Dogmas of Empiricism," in *From a Logical Point of View* (40), and the introduction to his *Methods of Logic* (39). A very readable exposition of Gödel's proof is given by Nagel and Newman in an article with that title (36).

There is a theoretical discussion of the paradoxes of logic in Chap. 2 of Ushenko's *The Problems of Logic* (46). Further discussion of the paradoxes, with many illustrations, can be found in Churchman's *Elements of Logic and Formal Science* (10).

QUESTIONS AND EXERCISES

I

1. What is meant by saying that truth is a property of sentences? In what sense of "true" do we say truth is a property of objects? Give examples from ordinary language.

2. Under what circumstances will the following propositions be true? (A) A redstart just flew in the window. (B) A minor is a person under 21 years of age. (C) $3y = 15$.

3. "The statement "$3 + 2 = 5$" is true for similar reasons as, say, the assertion that no sexagenarian is 45 years of age" (C. G. Hempel). Explain what is meant here. Do you agree?

4. Outline on paper the debate on the status of the law of noncontradiction, summing up the various positions as succinctly as possible. What position do you take? Give reasons.

5. Explain the distinction between analytic and synthetic (descriptive) statements. What is meant by saying that the statements of logic are analytic? Explain why the expression "$q \supset (p \lor q)$" is a tautology.

6. What limitations inherent in axiomatic systems does Gödel's proof reveal?

II

Examine the following puzzles. Locate and explain the paradox (if there is one) in each case. If you can, suggest a means of resolution.

1. The town of Alcala has only one barber and he shaves all those and only those who do not shave themselves. Who shaves the barber?

2. All words may be divided into two classes—autological and heterological. Autological words are those which themselves possess the property they designate. For example, "short" is an autological word because it *is* short. Heterological words, on the other hand, are those which do *not* themselves possess the property they designate. Thus "long" is a heterological word, for it isn't long. Now the question is: To which of these two types does the word "heterological" belong?

3. "The sentence you are now reading is false." True or false?

4. You have been engaged by the library of Union Theological Seminary to catalogue all those books in the library which contain no mention of themselves. When complete, your catalogue is to be published as a book and added to the library collection. You are now correcting the final proofs of your book. Should your catalogue list itself?

5. "All generalizations are false, including this one."

6. During the Second World War, Dr. R. V. Glencoe of Pelham Manor, New York, devised a warning device for use by the civil-defense organization of his community. The device was ingeniously constructed. It sounded when and only when *all* the sirens in nearby New York City were silent. One day Dr. Glencoe brought his warning device into New York City to demonstrate it before officials of the civil defense there. What did his warning device do when the city sirens were silent? Can you suggest a remedy?

7. Eisenhower: What Foster Dulles is about to say is false.
   Dulles: The President has just spoken the truth.

8. When he was a young man Socrates was told by Zeno of Elea about the race between Achilles and the tortoise. "Since you are such a slowpoke," said Achilles to his opponent, "I'll give you a head start. You start at point A on the track and I'll start 100 feet in back of you." So they did, said Zeno, and the race began.

Now in order to overtake the tortoise, Achilles had to pass through point A. But since it takes a little time to reach point A, the tortoise has moved ahead to point B. Again, in order to overtake the tortoise, Achilles must pass through point B. It takes him a shorter time to do this, but still time enough for the tortoise to crawl ahead to point C. The same holds for points D, E, F, etc., with Achilles unable to accomplish any more than to shorten the distance between himself and the tortoise ahead. So, concluded Zeno, Achilles never overtook the tortoise.

"But Zeno," young Socrates protested, "I *saw* Achilles pass the tortoise; with my own eyes I saw it."

"Impossible," Zeno retorted, "Logic proves that Achilles cannot overtake the tortoise. If your senses tell you otherwise, so much the worse for your senses!"

9

Induction

Induction has always been closely associated with the methods of observation and experiment in physical science. At the dawn of modern science, Francis Bacon announced that the inductive method of the new sciences would put to rout *deduction,* a mode of inference he associated with the excessive rationalism of the later Scholastics. Today we know that Bacon's conception of the methods of natural science as exclusively inductive rather than deductive was much too one-sided. For it seems that the more advanced a natural science, the greater the part played in it by deductive procedures. Theoretical physicists are not able directly to examine the highly conceptual entities they talk about; the basic propositions of nuclear physics concern thing-events like electrons and neutrinos which are unobservable. Nevertheless, conclusions may be *deduced* from the hypotheses of nuclear physics which *are* testable by observation and experiment. No science which purports to describe the world around us can do away altogether with inductive procedures.

What is induction? It is a mode of inference by which we proceed from observations of particular instances or cases to a generalization about all instances or cases of the same kind. This generalization may then be used *deductively* as a basis of prediction concerning future cases:

Induction ⎰ Certain A's have been examined, and have been found to be B's.

⎱ Therefore, all A's are B's.

Deduction ⎰ Therefore this new, unexamined A will also be B.

Suppose I test several samples of alloy X for conductivity of heat. My results being favorable, I conclude that alloy X is an efficient heat conductor, and I use this finding as a basis of prediction concerning the behavior of future samples of alloy X. Had I known at the outset that alloy X is one of a general type of alloys all of which have the property of high heat conductivity, I could have reached the same conclusion *deductively,* and spared myself the inductive procedure of testing instances—unless, of course, I wanted to *confirm* the deductive generalization by independent experiment.

We may consider the following general statements to have been inductively established, for in each case the generalization was preceded by observation or experience of a number of instances.

1. Human blood falls into four major groupings.
2. Bluefish always poisons me.
3. Tibetans have inferior mentality.
4. The specific gravity of gold is 19.3.
5. All men are mortal.
6. Comets move in elliptical orbits.
7. Once a thief, always a thief.
8. Swimming immediately after meals is dangerous.
9. The female mantis eats her mate.
10. All babies here are worthy of a prize.

Note that just because each generalization represents the conclusion of an inductive inference, it does not follow that each induction is necessarily sound. Some inductions are sound; others are not. We shall discuss at greater length below what it means to say this.

Are all inductions inferences from particular cases to *generalizations?* Many of our everyday inferences follow this form:

> Certain A's have been examined and have been found to be B's.
> So this unexamined A will also be B.

These inferences may be analyzed in two ways. (1) They are combined inductive-deductive inferences in which the generalization is *implicit.*

> Certain A's have been examined and have been found to
> be B's.
>
> (Therefore, all A's are B's.)
>
> So this unexamined A will also be B.

(2) They are inductions of a type which does not involve generalization—induction from particular to particular.[1] Current logicians, however, tend to regard all inductions as following the first pattern, that is, as inferences to generalizations. Assuming this first interpretation, the reader can then easily formulate the generalization implicit in each of the following inferences:

> You'll have some fine skiing weather this month; every
> January we've been up here, we've had excellent snow
> conditions.
>
> This cleaning compound has worked badly whenever
> we've used it; it will make a mess of your coat.
>
> I'm sure you'll find Miss Grandison satisfactory; we have
> always found her a reliable employee.
>
> Every payday so far this year old Tom's been drunk; he'll
> be high as a kite tonight.

It should be quite clear, and the reader has doubtless already observed it, that the premises of these inductive

[1] J. M. Keynes distinguishes between arguments based on the number of instances examined (induction by *simple enumeration*) and arguments based on *analogy*. Suppose I have examined an instance of A in which the properties of P, Q, R, S, etc., are conjoined. Let us say I have been particularly impressed by property X. Now when I come upon another instance of A together with its properties P, Q, R, S, etc., I infer that this instance of A will also have the property X. A social worker notices a high incidence of emotional disturbance in children of families marked by certain characteristics—parental conflict, overconcern, and so on. When he studies a set of families with analogous characteristics, he expects to find a similar incidence of disturbance in the children. A paleontologist finds a fossilized jawbone resembling that of a modern man; he concludes that the animal which possessed it was of the species *homo sapiens*. We argue from analogy, says Keynes, insofar as we depend upon the *likeness* of the instances; from simple enumeration or "pure induction" when we rely on the *number* of the instances. Yet the two modes of induction are closely connected. For, increasing the number of cases examined may confirm analogy; on the other hand, such increase may show up differences which observation of a small number of cases did not reveal. See Keynes, *A Treatise on Probability* (28), part 3.

arguments do not *logically imply* their conclusions. That is, simply because the tested samples of alloy X have the property P, it does not necessarily follow that *all* samples of alloy X have the property P. Nor does the statement "On warm, damp nights in the past, fireflies have invariably appeared" logically imply the statement "Fireflies *always* appear on warm, damp nights." "Some A is B" does not logically imply "All A is B." Since the conclusions of inductive arguments do not *necessarily* follow from their premises, inductive logic cannot be presented as a formal system. It was the hope of many early philosophers of science that induction could be arranged in an exact system comparable to deductive logic, with rules and operations of similar precision. It is now generally conceded that this task is impossible.

Because inductive conclusions do not seem to follow *necessarily* from their premises, must we then deny that there are any sound inductions at all? This would be hard to accept. For some inductions certainly do seem sounder than others, as a glance at the generalizations in the list on page 153 will show.

Induction Complete and Incomplete

At the outset, we should distinguish between two kinds of inductive inference. Consider one of the generalizations cited on page 153: "All babies here are worthy of a prize." Now let us assume that the judge based his decision on an examination of *each and every baby* in the room. Consider, again, a sergeant, ordered to report absences in his platoon; he notes that A is present, B is present, and so on down the line without exception. He reports, "All present, sir." Again, a boy returns from the store with a dozen peaches. Since he brought home some unripe ones last time, his mother checks the contents of the bag, noting that every peach is ripe including the twelfth. Then she says, "They are all ripe." Now what is common to these inductions? *Each and every instance of the kind of thing under investigation has been examined.* In schematic form:

$a_1, a_2, a_3 \ldots a_n$ have the property P.
$a_1, a_2, a_3 \ldots a_n$ are all the a's there are.
Therefore, all a's have the property P.

This type of induction is not of primary importance. First, it is hardly inductive inference at all, but rather a convenient summary of what we already know. Second, it is not easily had. In only a minority of cases are we lucky enough to be able to check each and every instance of the subject under investigation. Still, this type of summation has real, if limited, use. After Aristotle, who classified it, it was known as "perfect induction." A better name would be "induction by complete enumeration." We shall not discuss this type of inference further.

By far the more important kinds of induction—those we rely on most heavily in scientific investigation and everyday life—are of the type the ancients called "imperfect" induction, that is, inductive inference as passage from "some" to "all." When we conclude that the sun always rises, that water quenches fire, that gold is malleable, that men are mortal, we reach our general conclusion after having examined only *some* of the instances of the subject under investigation. We could not have examined *all* because there are indefinitely many instances. The schematic form of our inductions is:

$a_1, a_2, a_3 \ldots a_n$ have the property P.
Therefore, all a's have the property P.

Or, more succinctly:

Some A has the property P.
Therefore, all A has the property P.

For our purposes, we shall take the term "induction" to be synonymous with incomplete induction. The capacity to form general judgments is a characteristic of human intelligence, and without incomplete induction a large and important part of the generalizations of science and common sense could not be formed. Further, whatever problems and puzzles there may be concerning induction, they refer to induction by incomplete enumeration or by analogy, not to "perfect" induction.

Strict and Broad Inductions

Let us make one further distinction. Inductive generalizations may be put forward with one of two intentions. When we say "All A's are B's," we may mean "Each and every A is B without exception." The generalizations "All men are mortal" and "Parthenogenesis does not occur in humans" are of this type. Let us call this *strict* induction. But often when we assert that all A's are B's, we mean "Generally speaking, A's are B's." Entomologists say that the female praying mantis, after mating, decapitates and eats the male. But if a case were observed in which the female mantis did *not* behave toward her mate with such savagery, entomologists would not feel that the foundations of their science had been dealt a shattering blow. For the statement was put forward as a *broad* induction; that is, as a general rule, the female mantis behaves in this way. In any science where great numbers of variables are involved, generalizations are usually put forward as inductions of broad rather than of strict intention.

THE PROBLEM OF SOUND INDUCTION

The practical utility of inductive generalizations is that they enable us to predict future occurrences. If samples of iron melt whenever I heat them to a certain temperature, I can form a general description or "law" which I may then apply deductively to future instances of that metal. An employer, interviewing a pretty and unmarried girl, calculates on the basis of past experience that he can count on her presence in his office for no more than a year or two before she marries and goes off to make her own home. But how can we tell a sound induction from an unsound one? What gives us the right, in certain circumstances, to make use of general statements or "laws" for purposes of prediction, when only *some* of the instances have been examined? In the round of daily experience, we encounter many instances of inductive generalizations which we quickly recognize as doubtful. Such would be "Actors are superstititous" and "Vodka has no aftereffects." On the other hand, we tend to accept such general statements as "At standard pressure, copper melts at $x°$ C." and "All men are mortal" as soundly extablished. Yet in the case of both pairs of generalizations, only *some* of the instances referred to have been examined. How is it possible to distinguish a sound induction from an unsound one?

Tentative Criteria of Sound Induction

What justifies inductive generalizations is the *evidence* we have for them. Hence, in determining the criteria of sound induction, we shall have to examine the ways in which we can assure ourselves that the evidence on which we base a generalization is good evidence.

Let us consider an example of relatively unsound induction: "Tibetans have inferior mentality." Is it possible to specify *why* such an induction is weak? We might challenge it on the following points (passing over the ambiguity of the term "inferior mentality"):

1. *Insufficient Number of Instances Examined.* The person making the generalization is probably basing it on a limited number of experiences of Tibetan people.

2. *Existence of Contrary Instances.* We ourselves may know of a significant number of Tibetans who are intelligent.

3. *Variable Character of That Which the Generalization Concerns.* Intelligence in humans varies greatly, and past experience tells us that generalizations about human traits are frequently unreliable.

4. *Absence of Independent Confirmation.* Among the published studies of Tibet and the Tibetans, there is none which makes such a claim nor are there any independent inductions (such as "Tibetans have poor visual discrimination") to which the subject generalization could be related.

Now contrast with this relatively unsound induction the relatively sound one "The sun rises every day." Unlike the generalization about the Tibetans, there are good reasons to accept "The sun always rises." What is the nature of the evidence in this case?

(1) The sun has been observed to rise in the morning a very large number of times. (2) We know of no authenticated instance in the past when the sun did not rise. (3) The rotation of the earth is not a variable matter like the behavior of redheaded girls. (4) In addition, the statement draws independent strength from the fact that it can be *deduced* from the laws of planetary motion, laws which have independent inductive support by way of examination of other planets.

In our treatment of the examples above, we have tentatively isolated the following as criteria for sound inductions: (1) sufficient number of instances examined, (2) no contrary instances, (3) nonvariable character of phenomenon under investigation, and (4) independent confirmation by deduction from more general laws, those laws being confirmed by other evidence than that used to support the given generalization.

Now each of these criteria requires comment.

1. *The Criterion of Number of Instances.* First of all we should note the circular character of the phrase "sufficient number of instances." Granting that a sufficient number of instances would satisfactorily establish an induction, the question remains, "What *is* a sufficient number?" If this question could be answered, most of the puzzles concerning induction would evaporate. It would certainly be helpful if we could adopt as a universal rule a formula to the effect that the strength of an induction increases in direct proportion to the increase in the number of instances examined. That is, the more instances of A found to be B, the more likely it is that all future A's will also be B. But to adopt any such formula would be decidedly risky. For a large number of instances is not in itself a safe criterion for the soundness of an inductive generalization. True, the criterion of number of instances is often relied on in practice. After a number of obviously imperfect fillings ("If it had been only one, I wouldn't have

minded!"), we change dentists, if we are sensible. The respect shown to the theory and practice of a new training-school administrator grows with the number of delinquents rehabilitated by his new education therapy. J. H. Fabre's classic work on insects is the fruit of thousands of pains-taking and minute observations. In medicine, in the social sciences, and in many other fields of research, the number of instances examined is often highly relevant to the security of the conclusions drawn. Why then should one object to the formula: The more instances examined, the sounder the inductive generalization?

One reason for objection is that there are large areas of both practical experience and scientific investigation where the criterion of increasing number of instances simply does not hold at all. It takes only one or two painful experiences to convince us that fire burns painfully or that it is not a good idea to rely on recapped tires. On the other hand, examination of 200 crows, each of which is black, will not incline us to bet money on the soundness of the induction "All crows are black." In the more highly developed sciences, such as physics, the criterion of large numbers of instances examined is hardly ever used. Rayleigh and Ramsay, who discovered argon, weighed no more than a sample or two of the gas, and found the density of the samples to be about 20; this figure was then accepted as the measure of the density of argon.

By reason of subject matter, the social sciences rely more heavily on extensive sampling than do chemistry and physics. Hence it is of great importance that rules be formulated in the social sciences for obtaining *fair samples* of the phenomenon under investigation. It is one of these rules that *other things being equal, the reliability of a sample increases with an increase in the size of the sample*. To be sure, other things being equal, a survey of social conditions in Harlem based on examination of 2000 families would be more reliable than one based on 100 samples. But there comes a point in such surveys by sampling where the decrease in the margin of error achieved by increasing the number of instances examined diminishes to the point of relative uselessness. Then, too, the presence of the phrase "other things being equal" tells us that the rule of increasing number is of little value in isolation from other tests of fair samples. For the number of cases might be large, but poorly chosen, thus weakening the conclusion drawn from them. Hence the rule of increasing numbers is usually employed in association with other rules. One such rule is that of randomness: *The more nearly random the sampling, the greater its reliability.* The social investigator who confines his interviews to residents of Harlem who live on Edgecombe Avenue, say, would be no wiser than the housewife who took as typical the strawberries on top of the box. Another rule of sampling, closely related to that of randomness, is that concerning stratification: *A reliable sampling of a stratified group must reflect that stratification.* A social survey of Harlem families which failed to take into account the small but important segment of professional people in that area would be seriously defective.

2. *No Contrary Instances.* This criterion of induction is of more value destructively than constructively. As support for a generalization it has no more force than "No news is good news." In the case of the generalization "All A is B," the fact that no A has turned up that is not B does not of itself mean that A will never occur without B. It is said that some eighteenth-century logic texts contained the statement "All swans are white" as an example of a sound inductive generalization, citing as evidence the very large number of white swans observed and the complete absence of reports of swans of any other color. When the news came that Captain Cook's men had turned up astonishing numbers of *black* swans in newly explored parts of Australia, that particular example was hastily dropped from the textbooks. The moral of the story is that neither large numbers of favorable instances nor the absence of unfavorable instances can be considered as completely reliable criteria of induction.

3. *Nonvariable Character of the Phenomenon Under Investigation.* The weakness of an induction seemingly

well supported by favorable instances, and attended by no known unfavorable instance, can often be detected by attending to the idea of variability. The induction concerning the whiteness of swans is a case in point. Even if none but white swans had ever been observed, the nature of the phenomenon concerned—the color of plumage—should have suggested caution before generalizing. For the color of plumage is highly variable in birds in contrast to warm-bloodedness, which is constant: for example, finches appear in all shades from purple to yellow, but all are warm-blooded. In the example of the swans, we are not simply reminding ourselves of the possibility of variability. We are also throwing light on the infirm foundations of this induction by showing that it tends to be disconfirmed by a more general law. The whiteness of swans is a particular case of the color of birds, and the proposition "Color in birds is constant" is false. Hence the law "Color in birds is variable"; this has independent confirmation and thus tends to disconfirm the generalization "The color of swans is invariably white." Hence statements about invariable color in swans should have been suspect in advance, even if no black swans had ever turned up.

4. *Independent Confirmation by Deduction from More General Laws.* I can know of the explosive results of heating unopened cans of soup in two ways. The first is by painful experience. This is the way of simple induction. The second, and safer, way is by considering in advance the general law "Gases when heated expand," and deducing from it that I will have a minor catastrophe on my stove if I heat the unopened can on it. The method of confirming inductions by showing that they are deducible from certain more general and independently confirmed laws is one of the most powerful tools in the methodology of the natural sciences. What is the evidence supporting the generalization "All men living will one day die?" It is not only that a very large number of instances of men's deaths have been examined; that we do not know of any instance in the past of a man who has failed

to die. The statement draws enormous strength from the fact that it can be deduced from independently confirmed biological laws concerning higher organisms generally. Similarly, the knowledge that the properties of metals are relatively constant—in contrast to human traits, which are known to vary widely—can be applied to support the statement that the specific gravity of gold is 19.3.

However, even though an inductive generalization "All A is B" can be supported by deduction from an independently confirmed law "All X is Y," we should not forget that "All X is Y" itself rests on inductive evidence. Consider the statement "Ice is less dense than water." We can establish this generalization by direct induction by measuring particular samples of ice. In addition, we can *confirm* this inductive generalization *deductively* by showing that it follows from two general statements: (1) Water freezes at 0° C. (2) Water expands as the temperature drops below 4° C. Now, although the confirmatory procedure is deductive, the two statements which serve as premises themselves depend upon inductive evidence.

Is Fulfillment of These Criteria Enough? Hume's Objection

Some philosophers have said in the past, and some do still say, that it is not enough for an induction to meet these criteria of soundness. They say that an inductive generalization can conform to these tests—number of instances, no contrary instances, etc.—and yet not *really* be sound. Or, if meeting these criteria is what "soundness" means, they say, then "soundness" is not enough really to *justify* induction. The classic example of such a critic is the Scottish philosopher David Hume (1711–1776).

Hume called into question the reliability of induction generally, and the justice of his criticism is still a matter of debate among logical analysts and students of scientific method. According to Hume, the only reliable knowledge we have is that which we receive through sense experience.

But sense experience brings us in contact with particular and individual occurrences only. It never presents us with generalities.

When we make an inductive statement, says Hume, such as "The sun always rises" or "All larks build their nests on the ground," we are stating something *more* than experience tells us. We jump to a conclusion the evidence does not strictly warrant. What experience does tell us is that *in the past* the sun has always risen and larks have built their nests on the ground. So too do we know that in the past men have invariably died and hydrogen has proved inflammable. But experience does *not* tell us that the sun will rise tomorrow, that larks will build their nests on the ground next spring, that those men now living will die. Nor does past experience of hydrogen have anything necessarily to do with instances of hydrogen which have not yet been observed. *Because something has been noticed to behave in a certain way in the past is not in itself a guarantee that it will continue to behave that way.* In inductive inference, Hume reminds us, we *assume* that the same properties will occur in the future on the basis of the observation of constancy observed in the past. But this assumption is not justified by experience, since its justification would require observation of instances not yet observed. "It is impossible," says Hume, "that any argument from experience can prove this resemblance of the past to the future; since all these arguments are founded on the supposition of that resemblance."[2]

It is Hume's opinion, then, that experience gives us no warrant of certainty for inductive statements. Why, then, do we make them and use them so confidently to support our predictions, both scientific and common sense? Hume would have us believe that we make inductive generalizations through nothing more than the force of *habit*. A dog that has been fed at the back door every day for a year at five o'clock will sit there this evening at that hour the very essence of expectancy.

[2] Hume, *An Enquiry Concerning Human Understanding* (24), p. 37.

But the fact that he has been fed at that time in the past does not in itself constitute sufficient ground for the belief that he will be fed at five o'clock tonight, nor indeed that he will be fed at all. The situation is not wholly different with us humans. We make inductive generalizations, says Hume, through force of habit. That things have turned out in a certain way in the past *accustoms* us to believe that they will turn out that way in the future. But for this belief there is no real justification whatever.

Attempt to Justify Induction: the Uniformity of Nature

Since Hume's time, philosophers and analysts of scientific method have gone to considerable trouble to "justify" induction, that is, to find some kind of principle or ground upon which valid induction rests. One of these is the principle of the uniformity of Nature, a criterion associated with the English economist and logician, John Stuart Mill (1806–1873). "The proposition that the course of nature is uniform," says Mill, "is the fundamental principle or general axiom of Induction."[3] Natural events are not isolated bits of a miscellaneous jumble. They are part of a vast process of cause and effect. The principle of uniformity involves the *law of causation.* "The cause of a phenomenon," Mill tells us, is "the antecedent, or the concurrence of antecedents, on which it is invariably and *unconditionally* consequent." Observation of a very few conjoined instances of metal and heat convinces us that heat will melt metal. For we perceive that the melting and the heat are not just coincident, but elements in a causal sequence. Now Nature is a system of such causal sequences, a grand pattern of events which are not merely haphazardly associated but necessarily connected with one another.

According to Mill, the principle of the uniformity of Nature is the ultimate major premise of every inductive argument. It is the most general empirical proposition. Upon this principle depends not only scientific investiga-

[3] Mill, *A System of Logic* (34), p. 201.

tion, which presupposes it, but all conduct of practical affairs. An enormously large number of instances confirm this general principle, while no instances of which we have reliable knowledge run counter to it. The axiom of uniformity communicates its certainty to all less general laws and to the particular inductive propositions of the natural sciences. The causal connections investigated by these special sciences are particular exemplifications of the law of uniformity.

One of the common objections to Mill's use of the law of uniformity to justify induction is that this procedure involves a circular argument. For we are justifying induction on the strength of the principle of uniformity of Nature, but the proposition "Nature is uniform" is *itself* established by induction. Mill was aware of this difficulty, and argued that the law of uniformity was exceptional among inductive statements. He was convinced that the usual challenge offered to inductive arguments could not be brought against this single, all-embracing principle, unique in its comprehensive generality, verified by evidence from all possible quarters, with no known case to the contrary.

Nevertheless, most critics have continued to find Mill's principle of uniformity unsatisfactory as a foundation of induction. The law is too vague. It appears to be an empirical proposition, but it has a hidden analytic quality. It is close to being true by definition. For every event which appears to support the law is counted as a favorable instance. But if a phenomenon occurred which seemed to run counter to the uniformity of Nature, our conclusion would doubtless be that, if only we knew all the attendant circumstances, we should see that this too is an instance of Nature's uniformity.

Mill's law of uniformity is an attempt to formulate the belief all of us have that the world hangs together in some orderly fashion, and that the natural course of events shows patterns and periodicities upon which we may safely depend for purposes of prediction. But it is very difficult to state the grounds for this belief in terms of a single axiom. It is even more difficult to prove anything about the "order of Nature" by tallying instances of that order. Long ago, Aristotle had remarked the obvious uselessness of searching for a large number of examples to support statements such as "A body tends to fall toward the center of the earth" and "Fish have backbones." The function of simple enumeration in such cases, Aristotle thought, is not to *prove* anything, but rather to call our attention to the existence of certain general patterns in Nature. The role of induction is to nudge us into awareness of these universal natural features, the existence of which is presupposed by the special sciences. Aristotle did not believe that there was any need to prove by extended nose counting what any reasonable man could see for himself after he had observed a few cases.[4] Neither Aristotle nor Mill would agree with Hume's view—that mere repeated association in time and space of object A with property P is all that supports induction. But neither was successful in formulating a principle which clarifies the problem of why inductive reasons are good reasons.

MILL'S METHODS: THE CANONS OF INDUCTION

Mill's principle of the uniformity of Nature leads him to another approach to the justification of induction. Inductive generalizations, he says, are based on the assumption that there are events in Nature which are *causally connected*,[5] and it is possible to distinguish these from

[4] Because of Aristotle's belief that the role of induction in science is to enable us to "see" the universal pattern manifest in the particular case, his conception of induction is sometimes called *intuitive induction*.

[5] Earlier, Hume had perceived the close relation of the question of causality to the problem of induction and had subjected the concept of cause to his skeptical inquiry. Experience, said Hume, gives us no more rational justification for believing in the objective existence of a causal relation (A causes B) than it does for the existence of those general laws we try to establish by induction (All A is B). Experience may furnish us with numerous separate instances of A *attended by* B. (The sun shines; the stone is warm.) We may even discover in our experience *invariable sequences* in each of which A is followed by B. (Whenever the sun is shining, the stone is warm.) But each observation of B following A is always something separate and distinct from

events which are only fortuitously conjoined. The dark clouds are causally related to rain, while the phase of the moon is not. The presence of oxygen in the air is causally connected to the burning of wood; the presence of nitrogen is coincidental only. Now if we can formulate sound canons for identifying real causal connections in Nature—if we can find reliable ways of distinguishing causal sequences from merely coincidental association—then we must admit that some kinds of induction, at least, are justified.

Mill's methods, or Canons of Induction, are five in number: the method of agreement, of difference, of residues, of concomitant variations; an additional canon (discussion of which we shall omit) is formed by joint use of the methods of agreement and difference.

1. The Method of Agreement

If two or more instances of the phenomenon under investigation have only one circumstance in common, the circumstance in which alone all the instances agree is the cause (or effect) of the given phenomenon.

In the summer of 1956, there was a small outbreak of typhoid fever in New York City. Upon investigation, it was found that all of the victims had a common history of attendance at the same confirmation party, held shortly before they had fallen ill. Further investigation confirmed that the disease had been transmitted by one of the food handlers at the party.

Jevons cites the example of Sir David Brewster's inquiry into the cause of the iridescent colors of mother-of-pearl. Was it the chemical composition of the shell itself that produced this effect? Or was it some characteristic of the surface of the shell? Impressions of the mother-of-

---

the next. Causation is never observed by sense perception. What sense observation tells us is "A then B," "A then B," and so on; but no more than this. Now through habit we insert between A and B a convenient and fictitious "necessary connection," which we call a causal relation, and then we conclude that "A causes B." (The sun warms the stone.) But we do not find this necessary connection *in experience.*

pearl surface were taken in wax, and later a similar surface was contrived in metal. The iridescent color now appeared in three substances—shell, wax, and metal. Each had in common a finely grooved surface. It was concluded that this common circumstance was the cause of the iridescence.

Atherosclerosis is killing large numbers of Americans today. It is known that Americans have in common the highest protein diet in the world. So certain investigations have proceeded on the hypothesis that high protein diet is one of the major causal factors in arterial disease. Important, although incomplete, confirmatory evidence has come from recent studies performed on young American soldiers killed in the Korean war. These studies showed that, in many cases, their blood vessels were lined with lesions. The lesions contained fat and waxes, among them a substance called cholesterol. This fat is common in many foodstuffs and is notably present in meat, milk, and eggs, as well as in products made from these foods.

Limitations of the Method of Agreement. The method of agreement has some power to provide us with suggestions, hypotheses, and lines of inquiry to be pursued in the investigations of science and those of everyday life. But this power is so limited that *by itself* the method of agreement is ineffective either as a canon of discovery or of proof of a causal connection. The canon is formulated in terms of a test for *the* cause. But we know that the same event may be produced by a *plurality* of causes. Of course, Mill was aware of this difficulty and conceded that the first canon requires the second (the method of difference) as a supplement. But the method of agreement has an important further limitation. It is almost impossible ever to isolate one single circumstance which alone is common to several instances of a phenomenon. In the incident of the typhoid-fever outbreak cited above, it so happened that all the victims were members of the Jewish faith. But this common circumstance (as well as the fact that all the victims had backbones) was quite properly ignored by the investigators.

The difficulty of isolating *the* common circumstance

in several instances of a phenomenon under investigation was well brought out by the famous inquiry of G. K. Chesterton and Hilaire Belloc into the cause of drunkenness. They drank brandy and water and got drunk. They drank Scotch whisky and water and got drunk. They drank gin and water and got drunk. Observing that water was present in each instance of the phenomenon under investigation, they concluded that water is the cause of drunkenness, and solemnly resolved to avoid consumption of that liquid in the future.

2. The Method of Difference

If an instance in which the phenomenon under investigation occurs, and an instance in which it does not occur, have every circumstance in common save one, that one occurring only in the former, the circumstance in which alone the two instances differ is the effect, or the cause, or an indispensable part of the cause of the phenomenon.

Looking out his window one night, a man notices that the moon has a strange cruciform aura. In some excitement, he calls out to his wife downstairs to look out the living-room window. She reports that she sees nothing unusual about the moon. The man moves to another window, and the cruciform light surrounding the moon has disappeared. He goes back to the first window, and once more observes the original phenomenon. Suddenly he realizes that his window, though open, is screened. He raises the screen to find himself looking at a quite ordinary moon. The striking phenomenon, he realizes with chagrin, was caused by the screen's interference with the light of the moon.

During the Spanish-American War, it was suspected that yellow fever was transmitted by the bite of a mosquito rather than by direct contact with infected patients. In an experiment conducted by an American medical commission, three volunteers slept in a screened room with clothing that had been in contact with yellow-fever patients. None of the volunteers contracted the disease in these circumstances. Then one of the volunteers entered a similar room to which mosquitoes were admitted. He contracted the disease. This was evidence that yellow fever was transmitted by mosquitoes.

The ancient Greek physician Galen was feeling the pulse of a distinguished lady one day when someone came in and said he had just been to the theater, where he saw Pylades dance. Galen observed a sudden acceleration of his fair patient's pulse, and suspected that her illness was caused by her love for the dancer. On her next examination, Galen arranged that someone should come in and remark that he had just seen the dancer Morphus perform. This produced no marked quickening of the lady's pulse. But Galen noticed the same exaggerated reaction when on the succeeding day the name of Pylades was mentioned once more.

For years, a certain Chicago lawyer had suffered from exhausting fatigue at the end of his work day, a fatigue all out of proportion to the amount of work he actually did. His physician could find nothing wrong with him, and advised him to see a psychiatrist. Prejudiced against psychiatrists, the lawyer decided to experiment on himself. Changing his diet, taking more exercise, and increasing his hours of sleep did no good. Finally, it occurred to him to suspend smoking his beloved pipe. At the end of the month, the fatigue symptoms had markedly diminished. During the next four weeks, he resumed smoking his pipe. The symptoms quickly returned. He concluded therefore that his pipe smoking was the principal cause of his fatigue, and reluctantly put his pipe away until such day as he should retire.

Limitations of the Method of Difference. Like the method of agreement, the method of difference can provide us with tentative hypotheses as to causal factors as well as tentative confirmations of their existence. As Mill points out, the canon is particularly useful when employed in association with the canon of agreement to eliminate noncausal factors. But it is obvious that the canon of difference, as Mill formulates it, is far from airtight either as a method of proof of positive causal agents or as a method of their discovery. For the canon requires that the two instances—in one of which the phenomenon is present, in the other absent—have *every* circumstance in common save one. That this ideal condition is impossible of fulfillment is shown by the following example.

A health officer, investigating a case of mass ptomaine poisoning in a girl's boarding school in Poughkeepsie, New York, finds that of 30 girls who became ill, all 30 had partaken of the potato salad served the previous evening for supper. Of the 22 remaining boarders, all are well and none had eaten potato salad that night. The officer quite sensibly concludes that the potato salad contained the causal agent and orders laboratory tests to confirm this. Now the reasoning of the health officer is in the spirit of Mill's method of difference, but not in the letter. For if the formula of the canon is exactly adhered to, the officer would have to show that salad eaters and non-salad eaters had every circumstance in common save one. But this is absurd. The boarders differed not only in their eating of the salad that particular evening but also in their height, weight, age, disposition, and color of hair.

It is sometimes said that the value of the method of difference can better be seen when the canon is stated negatively: *Nothing can be the cause of a phenomenon if the phenomenon does not occur when the supposed cause does*. This is in accord with the following rough formula for the difficult notion of "cause":

> x is the cause of y, if when x occurs, y occurs, and when x does not occur, y does not occur.

3. The Method of Residues

Subduct from any phenomenon such part as is known by previous inductions to be the effect of certain antecedents, and the residue of the phenomenon is the effect of the remaining antecedents.

According to Jevons, "There cannot be a simpler case of this than ascertaining the exact weight of any commodity in a cart by weighing the cart and load, and then subtracting the tare or weight of the cart alone, which had been previously ascertained. We can thus too ascertain how much of the spring tides is due to the attraction of the sun, provided we have previously determined the height of the tide due to the moon, which will be about the average height of the tides during the whole lunar month. Then subtracting the moon's tide the remainder is the sun's tide."[6]

A cannon shot fired from a frigate at sea falls puzzlingly short of the Frenchman. Wind direction, elevation, and train have been taken into account, to no avail. Suddenly it occurs to Lieutenant Hornblower that he did not allow for the motion of the ship itself which serves as the gun's platform. On the supposition that neglect of this factor is the cause of the discrepancy, the requisite correction is made. Verification occurs as succeeding shots fall true.

Early in the nineteenth century, it was thought that Uranus was the outermost planet of the solar system. Its orbit was calculated on the assumption that its motion was determined only by the sun and the planets within the orbit of Uranus. But there was a discrepancy amounting to two minutes of arc between the orbit plotted on the basis of these calculations and the observed positions of Uranus. In 1845, the astronomer Leverrier postulated the existence of a planet, hitherto unknown, at some position in space beyond Uranus which was influencing its motion. The position of the hypothetical planet was plotted, and in 1846 a new planet, later named Neptune, was observed through the telescope within one degree of the predicted space.

Limitations of the Method of Residues. The method contains no rule for the discovery of the cause, this being found upon confirmation of a hypothesis independently drawn. In the case of the discovery of Neptune, the discrepancy between the calculated orbit and the observed positions of Uranus did not of itself point to the existence

[6] Jevons, *Elementary Lessons in Logic* (25), p. 253.

of a new planet. Even on the assumption that the cause of the disturbance was of planetary origin, the discrepancy could have been caused by two planets, although Leverrier was right in testing the simpler hypothesis first. Further, if a and c are followed by b and d, and a is known to be the cause of b, it does not follow that c is the cause of d, unless it can be proved that a and c are the only antecedents and that a is not also the cause of c. To use Eaton's example,[7] suppose we knew that two men entered a house at night and that two other men were found murdered there shortly afterward. Suppose we knew that A murdered B. Would it follow that A's companion, C, murdered D? No, for A might have murdered them both.

4. The Method of Concomitant Variations

Whatever phenomenon varies in any manner whenever another phenomenon varies in some particular manner is either a cause or an effect of that phenomenon, or is connected with it through some fact of causation.

A wife observes that the degree of her husband's cheerfulness varies inversely with the incidence of house visits from her mother. Very little imagination on the wife's part will suggest the hypothesis that her mother's visits and her husband's gloom are causally connected.

The phenomena known as magnetic storms produce compass disturbances and interfere with radio communication. For years, observations of the sun have showed that sunspots—dark areas believed to be titanic storms on the surface of the sun—increase at just those times when magnetic storms are producing fine displays of aurora borealis and disrupting wireless communications on the earth's surface. It is now generally agreed that magnetic storms on earth are caused by these disturbances on the surface of the sun.

There has been a remarkable increase in the incidence of lung cancer in the last 25 years. Mortality from the disease during this period has gained more than 500 percent. At the same time, there has been an enormous in-

[7] Eaton, *General Logic* (19), p. 533.

crease in the consumption of cigarettes. Statistical surveys in this country and in Europe have shown a high proportion of cigarette smokers among patients suffering from lung cancer, and a low proportion of smokers among patients without lung cancer. Many medical authorities have therefore concluded that smoking is a definite causal agent in the production of lung cancer, and have recommended for health reasons that the habit be curtailed.

Limitations of the Method of Concomitant Variations. The canon of concomitant variations, in the form of the method of statistical correlation, is widely used as an instrument of scientific research. As in the case of Mill's other methods, however, this canon does not nail down a positive cause but rather suggests a hypothetical cause, to be confirmed or disconfirmed by independent test. There is always the possibility of a plurality of causes to be considered in cases of apparent concomitant variations, as well as the possibility that the correlation is coincidental rather than causal. Statistical correlation does not necessarily mean a cause-and-effect relationship. For years, it is said, there existed a remarkable correlation between the price of rum in Cuba and the salaries paid to Presbyterian ministers in Massachusetts. Lunatics are so called because of a supposed correlation between their behavior and the phases of the moon. Because the increase in juvenile delinquency in the United States in 1942–1943 was paralleled by the rapid growth of the Women's Army Corps, it was actually suggested by a responsible personage that the latter was the cause of the former. Careless use of the method of concomitant variations often leads to the fallacy of the false cause.[8]

The validity of conclusions reached by the method of concomitant variations depends on the validity of the particular statistical procedures used in investigation of the phenomenon. Analysis of such procedures is obviously a separate and advanced field of study. That the technique and interpretation of statistical correlation is by no means a settled affair is illustrated by the quarrel among experts

[8] See below, Chap. 10, pp. 200, 201.

on the case of the correlation between smoking and lung cancer. The apparently high correlation between smoking and cancer seems to be supported independently by experiments in which mice painted with tobacco tar have developed cancer. Yet some objectors point to the fact that cigarette *paper* has not been eliminated as a causal factor. Others call attention to the fact that lung cancer is a disease of the later decades of life, and that the number of persons over 65 years of age in the United States has quadrupled in the last 50 years. Hence a substantial increase in lung cancer is to be expected, because of the far greater number of vulnerable persons. But American Cancer Society researchers reported in 1957 "a spectacular relationship" between cigarette smoking and lung cancer. Of 32,392 nonsmokers, only four died of lung cancer. But there were 265 cases among 108,000 smokers.

THE ROLE OF PROBABILITY IN INDUCTIVE INFERENCE

Many contemporary critics say that, whatever limited use Mill's methods may have as tools of scientific inquiry, they do not provide us with an answer as to just what, if anything, constitutes the ground of induction. That is, Mill's canons of induction do not furnish any answer to Hume's question: Why is it that on the basis of *some* examined instances ("Some horned animals part the hoof") we can reach a reliable conclusion concerning *all* instances ("All horned animals part the hoof")? As Hume says, we have not examined *all* of the instances. How can we tell, on the basis of *examined* instances, something concerning *unexamined* instances? How can we justify our belief that what has happened in the past will continue to happen in the future? Neither Mill's methods nor his general axiom of uniformity appear to provide an unshakable basis for our faith in the reliability of induction. In fact, it seems that we are just as far away as ever from proof that inductive inferences can ever be certain.

Faced with this attitude, many critics today agree with Hume that inductive inference can never give *certainty*. But the alternative, they say, need not be skepticism. If a generalization cannot be proved certain, at least it can be *confirmed* to a greater or lesser degree; if an inductively established law cannot be *certain*, at least it can be more or less *probable*. For example, we cannot say that the second law of thermodynamics is "certain," for the law makes an assertion about unexamined instances; so does the law of death, "All men are mortal." But since these laws have been confirmed time and again by experiment and deductive analysis, we may say that they possess a high degree of probability. It may not be certain that the sun will rise tomorrow, but it is highly probable that it will. On the other hand, the generalization "Humans have the power of extrasensory perception" has a distinctly lower degree of probability.

Probability and Numerical Value

The term "probability" is used to signify a property of inference, and its degree is considered to depend upon the nature of the evidence which supports that inference. Now if one hypothesis can be more probable than another, can we assign a numerical value to their probabilities? Is it possible to measure the "chances" or likelihood that an event, as yet unexamined, will occur, and to express that measurement by a precise figure? There is a discipline, generally considered one of the branches of mathematics, called "probability theory," and by means of "probability calculus" the likelihood of certain events happening may be expressed exactly in terms of a number between 0 and 1. Thus we say that the probability of obtaining tails on any given toss of a coin is one out of two, and that the probability of an American of a certain age and sex dying of heart desease is one out of four. Let us work out a few simple problems in probability calculus.

What is the probability of a penny turning up heads on any given throw? The answer is 1/2 because there are two ways the penny can land, head or tail, and the penny will have to land in one of the two ways. Thus the chances of getting heads are one out of two. We write this 1/2. The number of possible ways in which the penny can fall gives us our denominator, 2. The event in which we are interested (heads) can turn up in only one way. Thus we derive our numerator, 1. The probability of drawing a king from a standard deck of cards is 4/52; there are 4 chances out of 52 of drawing a king (4 kings in the deck; 52 cards in the deck.) We notice that numerical probabilities vary between 0 and 1. This must be so, for 1 would be positive certainty and 0 would be negative certainty. That is, the "probability" of throwing a 7 with a single standard die is 0, but the "probability" of a standard penny possessing one head is 1. Neither would be true probabilities; they are certainties.

What are the chances of throwing two heads in succession? This will clearly be less than the probability of getting one head. The answer is 1/4, because there are four possibilities for the two throws—HH, HT, TH, TT—and only one of them is what we want ("success").

$$P = \tfrac{1}{2} \times \tfrac{1}{2} \quad \text{or} \quad \tfrac{1}{4}$$

In the simple example above we can see an instance of one of the laws of elementary probability calculus, the product theorem:

$$P(A \text{ and } B) = P(A) \times P(B)$$

What is the probability of getting a 6 on the first throw of a die and a 1 on the second throw? The probability of a 6 is 1/6, and that of a 1 is also 1/6:

$$P = \tfrac{1}{6} \times \tfrac{1}{6} \quad \text{or} \quad \tfrac{1}{36}$$

There are 36 possibilities, and only one is success.

Now what is the proability of getting a 6 and a 1 in a single throw of two dice? The probability of getting a 6 on die X is 1/6; and the probability of getting a 1 on die Y is also 1/6. So the probability of 6 on Y and 1 on X is 1/36. But all we want is the probability of a 6 on one die and a 1 on the other; it does not matter which die the 6 or 1 is on. In other words, we want the probability of getting either a 6 on X and a 1 on Y or a 6 on Y and a 1 on X. A second law of probability calculus, the addition theorem, takes care of this situation:

$$P(A \text{ or } B) = P(A) + P(B)$$
$$P = \tfrac{1}{36} + \tfrac{1}{36} = \tfrac{2}{36} \quad \text{or} \quad \tfrac{1}{18}$$

It is easy to see how in this manner an elaborate calculus can be built up.

The method above of calculating probability is called the *a priori* method, and with good reason. For this interpretation of probability is a purely *deductive* affair throughout. It can be used to obtain a probability figure concerning actual events only if we make certain assumptions concerning our subject matter at the outset. What is it that enables us to assign such precise probability values to inferences conerning events that have not yet happened? The reason is that certain assumptions are made in advance concerning the behavior of the coins or dice. It is *assumed* that it is equally likely that the penny will turn up heads or tails. But the claim of equal likelihood of heads or tails is by no means a self-evidently true proposition.

Now if a priori probability calculations are made thus in advance of trial (and that is what a priori means), why is it that such calculations are so useful in predicting the properties of actual events such as the frequency with which a given face of a coin or die will turn up? The answer is that the behavior of the actual coin or die is so close to the behavior of the ideal ("equally likely") coin or die that for practical purposes they may be considered the same; the margin of deviation is negligible. Nevertheless, while a priori assumptions of the "equally likely" kind may result in little appreciable error in calculating probabilities in the case of simple objects such as pennies or dice, they can be very misleading when applied without care to more complex situations. There have been men rash enough to try by this method to calculate the probability of the existence of God.[9]

Probability as Relative Frequency

There is another way of interpreting probability, a way closely linked to familiar inductive procedures. This is to take the meaning of probability as *relative frequency*. Perhaps the simplest statement of probability in terms of

[9] See Lecomte du Noüy, *Human Destiny* (30), p. 35.

frequency is Aristotle's statement "The probable is that which usually happens." For example, in the case of any given human birth, the probability of the infant being a boy is roughly 1/2. In the frequency interpretation, this means that in relation to the total number of births (girl, boy), the frequency of boy births is such that it may be expressed by the approximate figure 1/2. This then is taken to be the probability of the birth of a boy in any given case.

Insurance companies set their rates on the basis of probability figures derived from tables of relative frequency. For example, a life-insurance company tells us that the chances are that three out of five men over age 40 today will die of cardiovascular-renal disease. Since such evidence is statistical, it can support no inference concerning the future fate of any individual man. The evidence for the probability figure 3/5 in this case is tabulations of relative frequency of deaths from this type of ailment. The computation is based on the population and death records for the total United States. Investigation based upon recorded deaths among the population of American males at ages 40 and over in a recent period shows that approximately 600 in each 1000 died of some form of cardiovascular-renal disease. These figures indicate that the frequency of such deaths is 3/5. The evidence is translated into the form "Three out of five men, etc." and is used for purposes of prediction. But insurance-company statisticians do not assume that the underlying conditions producing these observations will remain unchanged; rather, they expect change and base their projections upon trends and current developments which may affect trends.[10]

Let us apply the relative-frequency meaning of probability to our coin-throwing example. I am interested in determining the chances of getting heads. I complete a series of 1000 actual throws and note the results—506 heads

[10] Metropolitan Life Insurance Company, *Statistical Bulletin* (32). See also Dublin, Lotka, and Spiegelman, *Length of Life* (18), pp. 89 *et seq.*

and 494 tails. This gives us a relative frequency of heads for the 1000 throws of 506/1000. I now make a second series of throws. At the end of that series I find I have 1004/2000. My results appear to be converging on the limiting figure 1/2; this I take to be the *limit of frequency* of the favorable event—heads. I can, if I wish, carry out a further series of throws. If, after these further trials, the frequency of heads is still closer to 1/2, then my assumption that 1/2 is the limit was correct. If, on the other hand, a divergence becomes apparent, we will have to correct our original estimate.

Of course, a skeptic might object that it is impossible, strictly speaking, to say what the limit of the relative frequency is. Suppose we have thrown the coin a million times, and the relative frequency of heads is 500,021/1,000,000. This is very close to 1/2. But how do we know that if we threw the coin another million times, the frequency for the whole sequence would not be 1,500,021/2,000,000, which is not nearly as close to 1/2? That is, when we stop making tests, how can we be sure that if we went on the relative frequency would not begin to deviate drastically from the figure we had when we stopped? In point of fact, we cannot know this. To use Hans Reichenbach's expression, we just "posit" that the limit of the relative frequency is 1/2.[11]

Is Probability the Answer?

Let us return to the general problem of the role of probability in inductive inference. Does it help to say that while no inductive inferences can ever be certain, such inferences can in many cases be highly probable? If the probability of all inductive inferences could be calculated and expressed numerically, the problem of induction would be solved and human knowledge would attain an undreamed-of degree of order and adequacy. But there are countless inductions to which we cannot assign numerical probability at all. It would, for example, be impossible to

[11] See Reichenbach, "The Logical Foundations of Probability" (*41*).

determine that number between 0 and 1 which expresses
the probability of the following:

> Red hair is a recessive characteristic.
> Cancer is caused by a virus.
> All bodies are receding from the center of the universe.
> Humans have the power of extrasensory perception.
> Polar bears hibernate.
> Fifteen-year-olds resent parental interference.
> At sea level, the boiling point of water is 0° C. etc.

But even if we cannot assign a numerical probability to
the larger part of the inductions of science and common
experience, perhaps we can say that many of them are
probable in the sense that they are credible or likely—
probable more or less. That is, the proposition "All men
will one day die" is not absolutely certain, since the deaths
of future men have not yet occurred; yet in view of the
enormous positive evidence from past experience, the proposition has a very high degree of probability. This is fine,
for all but Humean skeptics. If knowledge of past instances,
they say, communicates no *certainty* to inferences concerning future instances, why should it communicate *probability?* For if we cannot know that all *A* is *B*, having observed
that some *A* is *B*, how can we *know* that it is *probable* that
all *A* is *B?* Are we to say that this also is only probable? If
so, we can only know that it is *probable* that it is probable
that all *A* is *B*. The reader can see for himself where such
a difficulty leads. If Hume is right, it should be hardly
less difficult to explain the probability of inductive inferences than it is to justify their certainty.

Can Induction Be Justified? Conclusion

Hume believed that induction had no more foundation than habit and expectation, that it rested at best
on evidence which is only partial, and that neither science
nor philosophical analysis could prove the certainty of any
induction. Ever since, philosophers, logical analysts, and
students of the methodology of science have tormented
themselves with the question "Can induction be justified?"

Mill's principle of the uniformity of nature was tried and found wanting. Mill's admirer, John Maynard Keynes, tells us that the "inductive hypothesis" is indispensable to science and common sense; yet this hypothesis, he says, stands in the peculiar position of being neither a self-evident logical axiom nor an object of direct acquaintance by sense experience. Still, Keynes assures us, our present inability to show the grounds of the "inductive hypothesis" is no reason for skepticism concerning its existence. "We need not lay aside the belief," he says, "that this conviction gets its invincible certainty from some valid principle present to our minds, even though it still eludes the peering eyes of philosophy."[12]

Peer as we will, philosophers or no, it is unlikely that we shall ever find this obscure principle which like a logical St. George will one day rescue human knowledge from the dragon Doubt. Once more, consider the following schema:

A number of A's have been found to be B's.
Therefore, all A's are B's.

As it stands above, schematically represented and taken abstractly, it is clear that the principle of induction has no justification. Induction *as such* is not *formally* valid. This we know by the enormous number of unsound inductions which are of the pattern above. Induction cannot be justified by formal means—that is to say, *deductively*—as we prove a syllogism valid or a truth function tautologous. "Some S is P; therefore all S is P" is simply logically invalid, no matter how many S's are P's. We cannot formulate induction as a deductive logical principle and apply this axiom to our investigations of the world's behavior in the hope that it will provide reliable security in inference.

However, the fact that inductive inference cannot have deductive certainty does not mean that inductive inferences cannot be parts of a system of concepts ordered in some way analogous to the structure of a purely formal system.

Finally, if we ask whether any inductive conclusions

[12] Keynes (28), p. 264.

may correctly be described as *certain*, the answer will depend upon the meaning assigned to the word "certain." If "certain" is used in the sense of ordinary certainty, the answer will in many cases be yes. We *behave* as if inductive reasons are good reasons. We *act* as if unexamined instances of water will be liquid at room temperature and a quantity of strychnine will kill us if we swallow it. Carrying on the business of science and daily life on the assumption of the reliability of induction *works*. But if by "certain" is meant *logical* certainty, that conviction which attends the inferences of mathematics and formal logic when correctly drawn, the answer will be no. Nor can inductive statements properly be called certain if by "certainty" is meant they cannot be corrected. We cannot claim that any inductive generalization is beyond correction or revision, or that the behavior of future unobserved instances can in any case be unconditionally guaranteed in advance.

BIBLIOGRAPHICAL NOTE

Aristotle's remarks on induction may be found in his *Posterior Analytics* (2), 99ᵇ 15 *et seq*. For Hume on induction, see his *An Enquiry Concerning Human Understanding* (24), pp. 37 *et seq*. Mill's treatment of induction is in Book III of his *A System of Logic* (34). On the topic of probability, Keynes' *A Treatise on Probability* (28) is a classic work. Recommended readings include Chaps. 8, 13, and 14 in Cohen and Nagel (11); chaps. 12 to 18 of Mace (31); Chap. 9 of Pap's *Elements of Analytic Philosophy* (37); "The Justification of Induction" by Black in *Language and Philosophy* (6); "The Justification of Induction" and "The Logical Foundations of Probability" by Reichenbach (41). See also Williams, *The Ground of Induction* (48).

QUESTIONS AND EXERCISES

1. Distinguish between deduction and induction. Give examples.

2. "The method characteristic of modern science is inductive." Criticize.

3. Illustrate ten inductive inferences you believe to be sound. Briefly discuss the evidence in each case.

4. Distinguish between induction by complete and incomplete enumeration; between strict and broad inductions. Give examples.

5. Distinguish between the two senses of "law" represented by (1) Newton's first law of motion, (2) a law passed by Congress.

6. Apply the criteria suggested on p. 158 to the following inductions: (1) "There is nothing more dangerous than Latin American food," (2) "Bears hibernate."

7. Give three examples of inductive generalizations strengthened by increasing the number of instances examined.

8. Why is a large number of instances examined not in itself a safe criterion for the soundness of an induction? Explain and illustrate with your own examples.

9. In the case of sampling, just what is meant by "random"? Illustrate. Give examples of samplings where the rule of randomness and the rule of stratification need to be applied.

10. Explain the role of the criterion of "no contrary instances" in induction. Use your own illustrations.

11. What is *intuitive* induction?

12. Cite your own examples to show the importance in inductive inference of the *variability* of the type of phenomenon under investigation.

13. From science or common-sense inquiry, cite three instances of inductive conclusions that can be confirmed by deduction from more general laws.

14. Explain and illustrate induction by analogy.

15. State Hume's objection to the validity of induction. According to him, what is the ultimate basis of induction?

16. Explain Mill's principle of uniformity of Nature as the ground of induction. Cite objections to it.

17. Why did Mill think that sound inductive inference depends on the existence of causal relations?

18. Give a good definition of "cause" with illustrations to support it. Cite Hume's objection to the validity of causal inference.

19. Make up two or three examples to illustrate each of Mill's Canons of Induction. Cite limitations of each of Mill's methods.

20. Discuss ordinary meanings of "certain," "probable," and "doubtful." Illustrate in each case.

21. "Inductive conclusions can never be certain; but they can be probable." Give reasons for accepting this statement and reasons for questioning it.

22. What sort of evidence would justify our calling the inductive conclusions listed on p. 182 "probable"? Discuss each case separately.

23. Distinguish between the *a priori* and the *frequency* interpretations of probability. Illustrate.

24. In each of the following examples, give the answer in terms of a fraction between 0 and 1. Assume equiprobability.
   1. What is the probability of getting an 8 on a single throw of a pair of dice? Two 11's in a row?
   2. Using two pennies, what is the probability of getting double heads three times in a row?
   3. You are playing bridge with three others. Dealer starts with you on his left. What is the probability you will be dealt four aces? That you will be dealt all face cards?
   4. Suppose a bag contains ten white balls and ten red ones. What is the probability of drawing two red ones in two successive single draws, assuming you do not replace the first ball drawn?
   5. Suppose a bag contains three white and two red balls. What is the probability of getting two white balls in succession in the first two drawings if the ball is not replaced?
   6. Make a drawing from each of two bags. The first contains eight blue beads and two red beads; the second contains six blue beads and four red beads. What is the probability that when we draw a bead from each bag, at least one of the beads is white?
   7. What is the probability of getting three 6's in five throws of a single die?

25. Do you think induction needs justifying? If not, why not? If so, what seems to you the best way or ways of justifying it?

10

Fallacies in Argument

> I love you
> Therefore I am a lover;
> All the world loves a lover
> You are all the world to me—
> Consequently
> You love me.
>   —J. G. VIVIAN

Since Aristotle published his short treatise on the fallacies (*De Sophistici Elenchi*), it has been traditional for logic books to include a section on unsound methods of argument. Strictly, analysis of some of these fallacies is the business neither of deductive nor of inductive logic; it is rather the concern of the classical subjects of rhetoric and argumentation, or of today's somewhat dubious successor to those disciplines—popular semantics. Still, logic *is* concerned with argument, and every well-educated person should be able to identify the common fallacies, even if this ability does not automatically help us to "think straight" or to become better citizens.

Fallacies in argument are divided into three kinds: (1) formal fallacies, (2) fallacies of ambiguity, (3) material fallacies.

The Formal Fallacies

From our study of syllogistic argument, we are already familiar with the formal fallacies. These fallacies are usually violations in ordinary discourse of the rules of the syllogism. Of the formal fallacies, those that occur most commonly in everyday argument are (1) improper conversion; (2) the fallacies of the undistributed middle and the illicit process of major or minor; and their equivalents in the hypothetical syllogism—the fallacies of affirming the consequent and denying the antecedent. The reader may review the appropriate rules. Here we shall discuss only the *undistributed middle* and its close relative *improper conversion*.

The fallacy of the undistributed middle is committed, as we know, whenever it is argued that because x and y belong to the same class or possess a common property, therefore they are identical. Because all gold glitters, it is not the case that this metal which glitters is gold. Because thieves are imagined to have a furtive look, it does not follow that Tom who has a furtive look is a thief. That Marxists supported the Loyalist cause in the Spanish Civil War does not make it valid to argue that Eva who supported that cause was a Marxist. The fallacy of the undistributed middle is implicit in much contemporary advertising. Thus it may be suggested (though not perhaps explicitly stated) that since successful men read the *Wall Street Journal,* a man who reads the *Journal* will be successful. It may also be strongly intimated that because certain lovely ladies follow a particular diet or use a particular scent, therefore those who do likewise will also be lovely.

The fallacy of improper conversion occurs when an *A* proposition is converted *simply* instead of *per accidens* (see p. 34). Here are three examples of the fallacy of improper conversion, for each of which we have invented an appropriate tag:

1. *The Fallacy of the Pharisee.* Because holy men bow their heads in prayer, and say "Lord, Lord!" those who bow their heads in prayer and say "Lord, Lord!" are holy.

2. *The Fallacy of the Patrioteer.* Since all who love their country should be willing publicly to profess their loyalty, therefore all willing publicly to profess their loyalty love their country.

3. *The Fallacy of the Bohemian.* Artists live in an odd fashion; therefore those who live in an odd fashion are artists.

The Fallacies of Ambiguity

These fallacies, which Aristotle called fallacies *in the language,* are all rooted in some kind of equivocation or double meaning.

1. *The Fallacy of Equivocation.* Sometimes called the fallacy of the ambiguous middle term, this is identical with a violation of the first rule of the syllogism (the fallacy of four terms). The fourth term is usually manufactured by using the middle term in two senses. This fallacy is committed whenever we allow the meaning of a term to shift between the premises of our argument and our conclusion. Thus to argue from the general consensus that people profit from the benefits of democratic government, that therefore the inhabitants of an eastern European "People's Democratic Government" enjoy the same or greater benefits, is to commit the fallacy of equivocation. For the term "democratic government" in the major premise of the syllogism implicit in the argument refers to democracy in the traditional Western parliamentary sense, while the governments of the so-called "people's democracies" have quite different properties.

Counsel for the defendant wins the sympathy of the jury when he argues that a person who "steps into the path of a car" has only himself to blame for his injuries. He then proceeds to show that plaintiff "stepped directly into the path of the car" in this case. The conclusion, "Plaintiff has only himself to blame," seems to follow inevitably. However, plaintiff's counsel rebuts the argument by showing that in the first usage the term "steps into the path of a car" is assumed to mean walking in front of an oncoming automobile, say, 40 or 50 feet away. But in this case plaintiff "stepped into the path of the car" only in the sense that he began to cross the street when the car was 200 feet away. To speak syllogistically, counsel for defense has used his middle term in one sense in his major premise and in another in his minor premise. Hence the fallacy.

2. *The Fallacy of Amphiboly.* Here the equivocation

or double meaning lies not in a term but in the syntax or grammatical structure of a sentence or sentences. A will with the following paragraph is badly drawn: "I give and bequeath the sum of $5000 to my cousins Ruth Henning and Sylvia Woodbury." Counsel for Miss Henning knows that deceased intended the cousins to share the money, but argues nevertheless that the sentence should be so construed as to mean that each cousin should have $5000.

Suppose in a murder trial a letter is introduced, written by the victim, which says, "Frammis plans to go to New York from Boston and then to Philadelphia by bus." We cannot conclude that therefore the defendant Frammis must have left Boston by bus. He might have planned to reach New York by some other means, and then to proceed to Philadelphia by bus.

3. *The Fallacy of Composition.* This fallacy consists in arguing that something is true of a whole which can safely be said only of its parts taken separately. We should not take jointly that which should be taken separately. In other words, we commit the fallacy of composition whenever we argue from a premise containing a term taken *distributively* to a conclusion in which that term is taken *collectively*.

Suppose A, B, and C offer independent testimony that the car driven by X was speeding. X's counsel argues that since every man is liable to err in such matters, the testimony of A, B, and C should be discounted. The court points out, however, that while A, B, and C are liable to error, taken individually, their convergent testimony, taken as a whole, does not have this same degree of fallibility, and should therefore be considered favorably.

Back in the 1930's, a new owner of a big-league baseball club reasoned that if he bought up the top stars of the league his team would win the pennant. Actual experience showed, however, that the inference was not justified. Because each player taken separately was an A-1 player, it did not therefore follow that the team composed of them was A-1. Similarly, a musical millionaire consumed with an ambition to create the best string quartet the world has ever known might reason badly if he argued that the way to fulfill his desire is to hire Oistrakh and Stern for violins, Primrose for viola, and Casals for cello. Although each of these virtuosos is unsurpassable, taken by himself, the quartet composed of them would probably be inferior to the old Budapest Quartet, the individual members of which were less brilliant musicians.

John Stuart Mill argues as follows for the proposition that the general happiness is the greatest good. "No reason can be given why the general happiness is desirable except that each person, so far as he believes it to be attainable, desires his own happiness. . . . each person's happiness is a good to that person, and the general happiness, therefore, a good to the aggregate of all persons."[1] But the truth of the second clause of the last sentence does not follow from the truth of the first. The good of each person, taken distributively, may be his own happiness; but it is not therefore the case that the general happiness stands as a good to all persons, taken collectively.

The Fallacy of the Drunkard is in effect the fallacy of composition. For the alcoholic who begs a drink on the plea that "one little drink won't hurt me" speaks the truth only if the drink is considered in isolation from others. Of course a drink in and of itself won't harm him; but taken in conjunction with the others he has absorbed, it may well do a great deal of harm.

4. *The Fallacy of Division.* This fallacy is simply the opposite of the fallacy of composition. It consists in predicating of the parts that which can be safely predicated only of the whole. That is, in such an argument we take separately what we ought to take jointly. Let us suppose (fictitiously) that the regime of the Republican party of Hither County, Long Island, has been marked by gross inefficiency and corruption for the past twenty years. It would be fallacious on that account to argue that Mr. Caspar Sanders, for many years town clerk of Longport, Hither County, and a Republican, is therefore guilty of inefficiency and corruption. Of course, neither does it fol-

[1] *Utilitarianism,* Chap. IV.

low from the data above that Sanders has *not* been guilty of these failings.

The Gambler's Fallacy may be construed as an example of the fallacy of division. The gambler knows that the probability of getting heads four times in a row is rather small. Therefore after three heads have turned up, he bets heavily on tails. For he assumes that the probability of heads turning up on the fourth throw is now considerably less than 1/2. But this is foolish, for although the probability of getting heads four times in a row is 1/16, the probability of getting heads on the fourth throw, taken by itself, is still 1/2.

5. *The Fallacy of Accent.* "This is a *fine* country to live in," growled the poor worker in Charlie Chaplin's film *The Great Dictator*. He was promptly arrested by the dictator's police, but managed to get himself off by pleading that all he said was, "This is a fine country to live in." Of course, the accent on the word "fine" was different in each case.

The fallacy of accent is committed whenever a second or unintended meaning is conveyed by misplaced accent in speech or writing. The clerk of court reads testimony in a deliberate monotone so that no inflection of his will convey an unintended sympathy to his hearers. It is said of Jeremy Bentham that so great was his fear of this fallacy that he employed to read to him aloud a man gifted with a peculiarly monotonous voice. The fallacy of accent is committed by critics who italicize portions of speeches or writings without acknowledging that the italics are not the author's. The fallacy is also committed by gossips who repeat statements made by some poor innocent in such a venomous voice as to prejudice their hearers completely.

Careless or slurred pronunciation may unwittingly generate the fallacy of accent. F. C. S. Schiller tells us that he once heard an audience of philosophers solemnly accept as an authentic quotation from William James the reading "If you are radically tender, you will take up with the Mormonistic form of philosophy." James, of course, had said, "more monistic."[2] Another writer confesses that through the years of his childhood he had cherished a silent devotion to a mystic, supernatural animal, holy though afflicted, which his church choir sang about nearly every Sunday. The animal so celebrated was "The Consecrated Cross-Eyed Bear." Alas for the illusions of childhood! It turned out that the choir was singing only about "the consecrated Cross I'd bear."

The Material Fallacies

According to the Aristotelian classification, the material fallacies are those which are "outside the language" (*extra dictionem*) in contrast to the fallacies of ambiguity which lie "in the language" (*in dictione*). Material fallacies are fallacies in the *matter* of the argument, rather than in the *form*. Such fallacies, however, should not be confused with errors of *fact;* the latter would be false statements rather than fallacious arguments.

1. *The Fallacy of the General Rule.* Sometimes miscalled the fallacy of accident,[3] this fallacy consists in arguing from a general rule to a special case. That is, we argue fallaciously when we apply a general rule without regard to the special circumstances which may change its applicability in the case we are considering. To argue that because parliamentary democracy is the soundest form of government, it should therefore be imposed upon peoples of primitive habits or with radically different political traditions would be to commit this fallacy. Because every man has the right to express his own opinions, it does not follow that therefore a judge should urge his own religious views in the courtroom.

In the realm of morals, the fallacy of the general rule may be identified with *rigorism*. It is, of course, wrong to steal. But to apply this rule to the case of a starving man who takes a loaf of bread from someone who does not

[2] Schiller (*43*), *Formal Logic*, p. 366.
[3] The classical name of the fallacy of the general rule is *secundum quid*. It is often confused with the unimportant fallacy of accident, also listed by Aristotle.

need it, no other alternative being available, is to measure a special case by a general standard. The "Other Wise Man" in van Dyke's tale knew that lying was evil, yet did not hesitate to misinform Herod's soldiery in order to save the life of a child. Note that this fallacy argues to a *special,* not merely to a *particular,* case. To argue from a general rule to a particular case is only to put a rule to the use for which it is intended.

2. *The Fallacy of the Special Case.* This is the converse of the previous fallacy; it consists in arguing from a special case or cases to a general rule. This fallacy is extremely common. I commit it when I argue that the employees of Macy's are discourteous because I was handled rather abruptly in the store during the Christmas rush; that the Sutton children are excitable and spoiled when I visit the family immediately after an exhausting birthday party; that Jones Beach is uncomfortably hot and crowded, after I drive there on a torrid mid-August Sunday afternoon; that liquor should be absolutely forbidden to young people because certain nonrepresentative members of a local fraternity have been abusing alcohol.

The fallacy of the special case is irritatingly frequent among persons who have lived in a foreign country for a brief time or in special circumstances, such as traveling with tourist groups or as dependents of military personnel overseas. Such persons will often confidently argue, on the basis of limited experience and special situations, to absurd generalities such as "They won't have anything to do with you unless you're a Protestant" (or a Catholic or a Buddhist, etc.), "They're absolutely inefficient," "They're immoral," etc. Those who commit the fallacy of the special case follow the fallacious rule of Aeneas, "*Ab uno disce omnes!*" ("From the one man know them all!")

3. *The Fallacy of the Irrelevant Conclusion* (Ignoratio Elenchi). This common fallacy occurs whenever we advance as an argument something that has nothing to do with the point at issue. A girl wishes to go to a dance with her young man, Jones, and mentions the fact to her mother. The latter replies, "You shouldn't go to the dance

with that fellow; his people made their money in the liquor business, and besides your cousin Alfred is such a nice
boy." The daughter is justified in pointing out respectfully
that while it may be perfectly true that Jones' people
made their money in the liquor business, and true as well
that cousin Alfred is a veritable pandemonium of virtues,
nevertheless these truths have nothing to do with the question, which is whether she should go to the dance with
Jones. The entire class of arguments by common prejudice
may be cited by all good liberals as falling under this fallacy. Thus we argue fallaciously that a man should not
have a job as a welder because his skin is black, brown, or
lavender. The point at issue is: Is the applicant a good
workman? To this point, the color of skin is irrelevant.
That Dreyfus was a Jew does not seem to us to be relevant to the question of whether or not he was a traitor;
yet thousands of his countrymen thought it was.

The fallacy of irrelevant conclusion is at home in the
courtroom, as anyone who has ever spent a day there can
testify. To protect his client against this fallacy, alertness
is required on the part of counsel ("Irrelevant and imma-
terial!"), fairness in interpreting the rules of evidence on
the part of the court, and good sense on the part of the
jury. A mass of irrelevant conclusions may be found in the
famous case of the *Commonwealth of Massachusetts* v.
Nicola Sacco and Bartolomeo Vanzetti (1920–1927).
These men were accused of killing a paymaster and his
assistant during the course of an armed robbery. It so happened that Sacco and Vanzetti were anarchists, and that
they were arrested at the height of a Red scare. An enormous quantity of testimony relating to their radical politics was introduced as evidence and admitted to the rec-
ord. The case was before the courts for seven years, and
in the end Sacco and Vanzetti were executed. The case
became a *cause célèbre*. Liberals correctly argued that the
political radicalism of the accused was fallaciously made
to bear upon the question of their guilt. Yet it was just as
fallacious to argue (as some overzealous liberals came
close to doing at the time) that because the accused were

"members of the working class" they could not possibly have committed the murder.[4]

Many varieties of the irrelevant conclusion have been distinguished and given separate classical tags. For example:

1. *Argumentum ad Hominem.* We argue *ad hominem* when we try to refute an argument by arguing against the character of the man who brings it forward or his dubious motives in so doing. If a senator were to urge the passage of a public-housing bill, it would be *ad hominem* to argue against him that his personal fortune makes it unlikely that his real motives are in any way connected with sympathy for the underprivileged. However, like many of the so-called fallacies in argument, *ad hominem* may under certain circumstances be both effective and legitimate. An ancient example of a sound *ad hominem* is the argument of Jesus against the self-appointed executioners of the woman taken in adultery. "He that is without sin among you, let him first cast a stone at her."[5]

2. *Argumentum ad Populum.* This variety of irrelevant conclusion is committed by anyone who addresses a mass audience and endeavors to sway the judgment of those present by appeal to matters close to their prejudices and emotions but separate from the point at issue. An orator or editor who argues against desegregation of public schools on the ground that such measures threaten racial purity must answer to the charge of this fallacy. So too must the politician who defends himself against accusation of taking bribes from contractors by arguing to (a) the sanctity of his family life, (b) the war records of his sons, and (c) his goodness to the poor. Like Bergson's orator, such a man falls in with the passions of his audience only in order to master them.

3. *Tu Quoque.* This argument, which amounts to saying, "You yourself do it," consists in trying to show that an opponent's argument against an action is worthless be-

---

[4] See Frankfurter, *The Case of Sacco and Vanzetti* (21).
[5] John 8:7.

cause the opponent has himself performed the same or a similar action. An instance of this would be to urge against a general's plea that mass bombing be avoided the point that the general himself ordered such a bombing in the last war. *Tu quoque* arguments are by no means always fallacious. What one's opponent has done in a similar case is often quite relevant to the point at issue, particularly if the opponent is a hypocrite. Again Scripture provides a well-known example. When legalists argued that it was wrong to heal on the Sabbath, Jesus pointed out that the legalists would be the first to haul out one of their sheep if it fell into a pit on the Sabbath.[6] The ancient story of the mother crab and her son also shows the power of the *tu quoque* argument. A mother crab said to her offspring, "Son, don't walk sideways like that; it's very awkward. Walk straight forward. That's the way to have an elegant appearance." To which the young crab replied, "But mother, *you* walk sideways."

Generally speaking, pinning the label "irrelevant conclusion" on any argument should be backed by our ability to prove that what is brought forward *is* irrelevant. Analysis of this fallacy tells us only that *if* a man offers an argument that is irrelevant, then he argues badly. But such analysis does not tell us *how* to determine whether a proposition is irrelevant. In certain contexts, a man's color, religion, or personal character may be quite pertinent to the issue under discussion. To settle the question of relevancy, further argument is in order.

4. *Begging the Question* (Petitio Principii). This fallacy occurs in any argument in which we assume as true what is to be proven. Suppose an argument takes this form:

$$A \text{ is } B.$$
$$\underline{C \text{ is } A.}$$
$$\therefore C \text{ is } B.$$

The argument is formally valid. But, as we know, for an argument to be materially sound, the truth of the prem-

[6] Matthew 12:11.

ises must be well established. Now suppose we prove the major by the proposition "C is B." We then have the following situation:

A is B.
(because A is C and C is B.)
C is A.
∴ C is B.

The circular nature of the argument is now apparent. For in order to prove the conclusion "C is B," the truth of that proposition has been assumed in the major premise.

Suppose I prove the existence of God by appeal to Scripture. But, someone tells me, the authority of Scripture has been challenged. I then proceed to establish the reliability of Scripture by arguing that these writings were divinely inspired. Here the fallacy takes the simple form known as *circle in the proof:* I have proved A by B; I then prove B by A.

Here is another obvious example of circle in the proof. Suppose X urges that the regimes of Trujillo and Batista be repudiated by our government. He gives as his reason that these regimes are military dictatorships and as such should not be tolerated. Asked to state the grounds of his objections to military dictatorships in Latin America, X replies, "They are the sort of governments that produce leaders like Trujillo and Batista."

Another species of begging the question might be called the *disguised circle.* Here A is proved by B; but B is really an altered form of A. Here are two obvious examples which would hardly deceive anybody. A philosopher wishes to prove the immortality of the soul. His argument runs: "The human soul is immortal, for not a shadow of a doubt exists that the noble spirit which animates the human clay will survive the catastrophe of death and continue to exist for all eternity." An orator is determined to establish the proposition that freedom of speech is for the common good. He argues, "Freedom of speech is for the common good, because the unrestrained expression of our opinions is ultimately to the best interest of all concerned."

Of course these are not proofs at all, for the argument which allegedly proves the proposition is only a restatement of that proposition in other words.

Disguised circles occur in all explanations that follow the pattern of Molière's physician who accounted for the sleep-giving power of opium by stating that the drug possesses "a dormative virtue." Similarly foolish is it to argue that bodies fall because they have a "downward tendency." In fact, all explanations of a particular property of X by arguing that it is the nature of X to have such a property run the risk of circularity. The reader should examine for circularity as well all arguments in social science which attempt to explain a type of behavior on the ground that there is a "need" for it. Any explanation of suicide by the reason that the deceased had a "death wish" should also be looked at rather carefully.

A common form of the general fallacy of begging the question is the *question-begging epithet*. Here the truth of the argument's conclusion is assumed in one word or phrase which occurs in the premises of the argument. A speaker who urges that a certain proposal be repudiated on the ground that it is "un-American" is using a very common question-begging epithet. It begs the question because the speaker and his audience agree to begin with that what is "un-American" is undesirable. What the speaker should prove is that the proposal *is* un-American. Such a proposition, however, is almost always incapable of proof because of the hopeless ambiguity of the term "un-American."

Finally, the question-begging epithet may be illustrated by reference to a recent debate on progressive versus traditional educational methods. One speaker arose to prove his point that the methods of traditional education are the more desirable on the ground that "Children cannot have too much of the right kind of education." But the word "right" assumes as true what is to be proven.

Does the syllogism itself as a mode of argument commit the fallacy of begging the question? John Stuart Mill thought it did, for this reason: Consider the syllogism:

All horned animals part the hoof.
The deer is a horned animal.
∴ The deer parts the hoof.

Now in order to establish the truth of the major premise, says Mill, the truth of the conclusion must be assumed.[7] For how could we know that all horned animals part the hoof unless we already knew that the deer had this property?

In answer to Mill's charge of *petitio principii* against the syllogism, two points are commonly made. First, in order that a syllogistic argument be sound, we need not *personally establish* the truth of the premises. From the statement in my zoölogy book that horned animals part the hoof, I may correctly argue by means of a syllogism in BARBARA that the deer parts the hoof. I did not establish my major premise by personal investigation, but rather drew it from a store of accumulated knowledge which I had every reason to deem reliable. Hence my syllogism, as an argument, has not begged the question. Second, the charge of begging the question can stand only if it is assumed that the major premise of a syllogism is established inductively by *complete enumeration*. Now this may be the case in the syllogism concerning the horned animals, for we would not say, "All horned animals part the hoof," unless each species of horned animals had been examined, including the deer. But only a minority of syllogistic arguments have this type of major premise. From the statement in my laboratory manual that the melting point of silver is $x°$ C., I may correctly argue that the melting point of this rod of pure silver is also $x°$ C. In this instance, my major premise is of the type of the great majority of inductions of science and common sense. That is, it is a generalization established by incomplete enumeration. Since a sound inductive premise can be established without complete enumeration, it follows that the syllogism need not commit the fallacy of *petitio principii*.

5. *False Cause.* Although Aristotle made a distinction

[7] Mill, *A System of Logic* (*34*), Book II, Chap. 3, I. The example is not Mill's.

between them, the fallacy of the false cause has come to be identified with the fallacy of *Post hoc, ergo propter hoc* (after this, therefore because of this). We commit this fallacy whenever we argue that since a certain event was preceded by another event, therefore the preceding event was the cause of it. That is, A is followed by B; therefore A is the cause of B. A very large number of superstitions probably had their origin in this fallacy. Because eclipses, black cats, and broken mirrors preceded catastrophes, it was fallaciously argued that these circumstances caused them.

In New York City some years ago there was a minor outbreak of smallpox. Mass vaccinations were ordered by the health commissioner, Dr. Weinstein. Soon outraged citizens were accusing the health authorities of using deadly vaccine. As proof they pointed to the deaths of hundreds of vaccinated persons within a period of weeks. Dr. Weinstein had to remind the frightened citizens that in a city as large as New York hundreds of people die anyway, in a similar time period, of many different causes. Because of precautions taken, a large number of those who died of other causes at this particular time were vaccinated. But simply because vaccination preceded their deaths, it did not follow that it was the cause of their deaths.

The Navy tells its potential officers of the deck the following story by way of warning. Once in a foreign port, a group of enlisted men returned aboard their destroyer after liberty. The men were obviously the worse for drink. As he passed the officer of the deck, one sailor slumped unconscious at his feet and could not be aroused. The OD had the man taken below and left in his bunk "to sleep it off." Next morning the man was found dead. Upon examination, it was found that his skull was fractured—the result of a chance blow in a brawl ashore. The officer was guilty, of course, of the fallacy of the false cause. Simply because the sailor's unconsciousness followed his drinking, it was unsafe to conclude that drink was the cause of his unconsciousness.

6. *Many Questions.* This fallacy is committed when we use in argument an apparently single question which is really composed of two or more separate questions. An example would be, "Have you renounced the habit of using narcotics?" The question cannot be answered yes or no, because it is two questions asked in the form of one, each of the two requiring a separate answer. The first is, "Did you ever have the habit of using narcotics?" The second, which *assumes* an affirmative answer to the first, is, "Have you given up this habit?" In the courtroom, where temptation to this fallacy is considerable, counsel must be on the alert to protect his client against such queries as "Did you or did you not visit the apartment of the deceased on the night of February 13, 1957, and there hold a conversation with him which led to a violent quarrel? Answer yes or no!"

As a concluding example, a question may be cited from an examination paper given in a course by an eminent Columbia professor. The question was: "List those books from the reading list you particularly disliked. To what defect in your character do you attribute this feeling?"

BIBLIOGRAPHICAL NOTE

The original classification of the fallacies is in Aristotle's treatise *On Sophistical Refutations* (*De Sophistici Elenchi*) (2). For further illustration of these fallacies, the reader may consult any good classical text. In nineteenth-century works, there are excellent chapters on the fallacies in De Morgan's *Formal Logic* (13) and Jevons' *Elementary Lessons in Logic* (25). In Book V of his *A System of Logic* (34), Mill offers his own classification of the fallacies. A large number of contemporary logic texts contain chapters on the fallacies, but many of the illustrations are trivial. A recent popular book on the fallacies in argument is Chase's *Guides to Straight Thinking* (9).

QUESTIONS AND EXERCISES

There is no better exercise in the identification of the classical fallacies in argument than making a personal collection and analysis of these fallacies. Accordingly, the reader is asked to find for himself in the field of his own experience and reading one or more examples of each of the following fallacies.

1. Undistributed middle

2. Equivocation

3. Amphiboly

4. Composition

5. Division

6. Accent

7. The general rule

8. The special case

9. Irrelevant conclusion (the general fallacy)

10. *Argumentum ad populum*

11. *Tu quoque*

12. *Argumentum ad hominem*

13. Begging the question (the general fallacy)

14. Disguised circle

15. Question-begging epithet

16. False cause

17. Many questions

Appendix

Logical Machines

In the past ten years there has been an enormous increase of interest in a subject that was once considered a minor academic curiosity. That subject is logical machines. The reason for current interest in these devices is by no means purely theoretical. A number of logical calculators have been developed by industrial-research centers and are now being used to solve technical problems in certain areas of science and industry.

What is a logical machine? It is any device that will solve a problem in formal logic by mechanical or electrical means. Credit for the first true logical machine is often given to the Englishman Charles Stanhope (1753–1816), who made a rather crude calculator, called the Stanhope Demonstrator, which solved syllogistic problems. In 1870, the English economist and logician W. S. Jevons (1835–1882) introduced to the Fellows of the Royal Society his "Logical Machine." Jevons had been impressed by Boole's logical algebra, but thought it was too complicated. Accordingly, he devised a machine to perform (as he thought) all the work of inference which in Boole's system was performed by "complex mathematical calculation." In the front of Jevons' machine were certain movable wooden rods which carried a set of 16 combinations of the letters A, a, B, b, C, c, D, d. The capitals stood for class names, the small letters for their negatives. Eight keys toward the left hand were marked with these letters and stood for these terms when occurring in the subject of a proposition. Eight other keys on the right hand represented these terms when occurring in the predicate of a proposition. A key in the middle represented the copula of the proposition. Still another key represented the disjunctive connective "or." Taking a syllogism or related argument, and turning its terms into A, B, C, D, or their negatives a, b, c, d, the Jevons "logical piano" could test for all possible valid combinations of these terms in syllogistic arguments. Ingenious as the Jevons machine was, it was not equal to handling more than a fraction of the logical problems generated in that system which has come to be known as Boolean algebra.

In our own century, particularly after the Second World War, the immense advances in electronics opened the way for the development of electronic calculating machines of all types. The proliferation of mathematical computers has been, of course, most spectacular; but side by side with the development of these computers was a growing interest in purely logical calculators. In 1938, Claude E. Shannon, a research assistant in electrical engineering in the Massachusetts Institute of Technology, wrote a paper, "A Symbolic Analysis of Relay and Switching Circuits" (*44*). In this paper Shannon pointed out the possibilities of exploiting the remarkable analogy between logical truth-function connectives and the conditions of switches and relays. In 1947, two Harvard undergraduates, T. A. Kalin and William Burkhart, impatient with the laborious construction of truth tables by hand required by their logic course, built a logical calculator out of material costing approximately $150. The Kalin-Burkhart calculator could evaluate logical formulae containing up to 12 terms. These and similar researches attracted the attention of scientists and engineers in industrial-research centers. Today there are a number of devices used in science and industry which accomplish their results by a logic function approach.

Described below are two logical machines. The first is a simple machine for testing the validity of categorical syllogisms. This machine, or one similar to it, could be made for a few dollars by anyone with a knack for wiring and handling a screwdriver. The second machine is far more complex, and tests long strings of logical formulae in modern notation. Logical calculators of this type can be used in research and industry to solve certain complex problems concerning the condition of switches, relays, voltages, pulses, and so forth.

Constructing a Syllogism Testing Machine

A simple machine for testing categorical syllogisms for validity can be constructed from parts whose total cost is about $15. The parts needed are:

4 Mallory ceramic wafer (nonshorting) switches:
   #1. 1 single gang (3215J); 1 pole; 5 positions.
   #2. 1 multi-gang (1325L); 4 poles; 5 positions.
   #3. 1 multi-gang (1345L); 8 poles; 5 positions
   #4. 1 multi-gang (1356L); 10 poles; 6 positions.
1 SPST toggle switch.
1 chassis; ICA metal, zinc-plated steel or aluminum. Dimensions 2″ x 5″ x 14″.
2 NE-51 neon pilot bulbs.
2 pilot light assemblies with 1 clear jewel and one red jewel with bayonet mount to fit NE 51 neon bulbs; DIALCO miniature type, series 810.
1 90-volt Burgess B battery, type N60.

The syllogism testing machine consists basically of two parts: a switching network and a neon lighting circuit. The switching network is composed of four Mallory switches altered as follows:

$$
\begin{aligned}
s_1 &= 1 \text{ pole} && 4 \text{ position} \\
s_2 &= 4 \text{ pole} && \text{``} && \text{``} \\
s_3 &= 8 \text{ pole} && \text{``} && \text{``} \\
s_4 &= 9 \text{ pole} && \text{``} && \text{``}
\end{aligned}
$$

The lighting circuit consists of two neon (NE 51) bulbs and a 90-volt battery; this is connected in series to the switching network to allow only one bulb at a time to light. The two indicator lights represent the valid and invalid condition of the syllogism; clear and red glass covers are installed over the lights on the front panel of the machine.

When mounted on its metal chassis, with dial handles put on and lettering completed, the syllogism testing machine will look like the illustration below. The dimensions will be that of a box about $15″ \times 7″ \times 3″$.

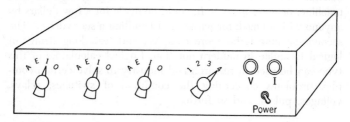

The first three switches prepresent the major premise, minor, and conclusion respectively. The fourth switch designates the four possible figures. The first three switches have four positions each, labeled A, E, I, and O respectively; these stand, of course, for the universal affirmative, universal negative, particular affirmative, and particular negative propositions.

Information is fed into the machine by setting the letter designator of each proposition of the syllogism (A, E, I, O) on the first, second, and third switches respectively. The figure of the syllogism is set on the fourth switch in either position 1, 2, 3, or 4. For example, take the syllogism:

> No members of the finance committee can be members of the social committee.
> All members of the finance committee are members of the executive committee.
> _____
> No members of the executive committee can be members of the social committee.

The syllogism is identified and coded as EAE (3), and the switches are set accordingly:

s_1	pos 2	E
s_2	pos 1	A
s_3	pos 2	E
s_4	pos 3	3

The invalid (red) light will operate. A syllogism in BARBARA, coded AAA (1), and set on the machine, will produce the white light; this is true of all other syllogisms valid according to the classical rules, including syllogisms with weakened conclusions and strengthened premises.

It is evident that all conclusions of "valid" and "invalid" are predetermined and built into the machine. Theoretically, a switching network which is devised to test all 256 categorical syllogisms should be composed as follows:

s_1	1 pole	4 positions
s_2	4 pole	4 positions
s_3	16 pole	4 positions
s_4	256 pole	4 positions

But such a network would be cumbersome and impractical. So several short cuts are used in designing the circuit. For example, in cases where a syllogism is invalid in all four figures, as in mood IEO, s_4 can be by-passed and the wiring led directly to the invalid line. In cases where no conclusion could be drawn (e.g., syllogisms with two particular and two negative premises), s_3 and s_4 are by-passed. Conversely, if the Syllogism is valid in all four figures (e.g., EAO, EIO), s_3 and s_4 are by-passed, and

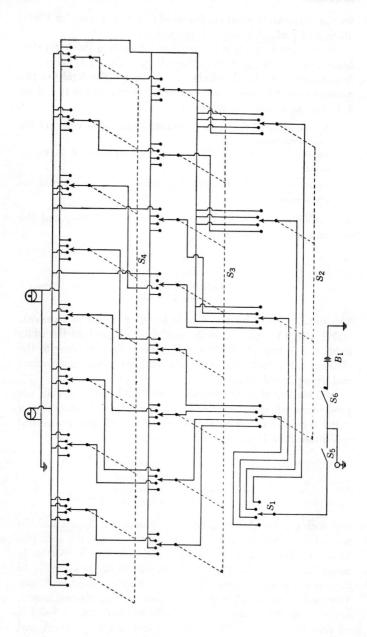

the live line led directly to the valid terminal strip. The total number of bypasses in the machine are as follows:

s_1	no bypasses
s_2	8 bypasses to invalid
s_3	21 bypasses to invalid
	2 bypasses to valid
s_4	19 bypasses to invalid
	16 bypasses to valid

The complete circuit schematic is given on p. 208.

A Machine for Testing Truth Functions

Contrasting in size and complexity with the simple syllogism machine described above are the large logical calculators now being introduced in modern science and industry. These machines are built to solve complex problems of formal logic, and to be set tasks ranging from checking conditions of electrical circuits to computations in genetics or insurance. Typical of such logical calculators is the Burroughs Truth Function Evaluator developed by the Burroughs Corporation at its research center in Paoli, Pennsylvania.[1] (See the photographs facing p. 210.) Among other uses, this machine can be employed to determine consistence or equivalence between two laws or statutes, and to test the applicability of provisions in these laws to contracts, wills, etc.

The Burroughs calculator evaluates truth functions and formulas made up of a string of such functions. The six functions which can be directly evaluated are:

> N—negation, not
> A—alternation, inclusive disjunction, either or both
> R—exclusive disjunction, either-or and not both
> K—conjunction, and, both
> E—biconditional, material equivalence, if and only if
> C—conditional, material implication, if, then

The formula to be plugged up on the machine must be expressed in Polish notation. In Polish notation, a formula is written and read from right to left. Instead of writing a connective (operator) *between* the variables, such as $p \lor q$, it is written to the *left*,

---

[1] The material in this section has been taken from William Miehle's paper, *Burroughs Truth Function Evaluator*, copyright, 1955, Burroughs Corporation, and is used by permission of the Burroughs Corporation.

Apq. The advantage of this notation is that it dispenses with parentheses and can easily be set up on a machine. The six functions may be listed on a truth table in Polish notation, thus ("False" is 0 and "true" is 1):

p	q	Np	Apq	Rpq	Kpq	Epq	Cpq
0	0	1	0	0	0	1	1
0	1	1	1	1	0	0	1
1	0	0	1	1	0	0	0
1	1	0	1	0	1	1	1

Let us take the formula $-p \lor q$, which we know to be equivalent to $p \supset q$:

$$p \supset q \equiv -p \lor q$$

In Polish notation this is:

$$E\ C\ p\ q\ A\ N\ p\ q$$

The whole formula is written right to left. This formula has a length of eight and two variables, p and q. Since both expressions which compose this formula are logically equivalent, the formula as a whole is true (or 1) for all combinations of truth values of p and q. In other words, it is a tautology. The truth-function evaluator takes 12 seconds to prove this formula a tautology.

Consider the fomula $-(-p \lor -q)$. We know that this, by De Morgan's law, is equivalent to $p \cdot q$

$$-(-p \lor -q) \equiv p \cdot q$$

Translating into Polish notation, we have $E\ N\ A\ N\ p\ N\ q\ K\ p\ q$. This formula has a length of ten and two variables, p and q. Here is its truth table:

p	q	1 E	2 N	2 A	3 N	3 p	2 N	2 q	1 K	2 p	1 q
0	0	1	0	1	1	0	1	0	0	0	0
0	1	1	0	1	1	0	0	1	0	0	1
1	0	1	0	1	0	1	1	0	0	1	0
1	1	1	1	0	0	1	0	1	1	1	1

We notice here that several results are stored up before being used. The maximum number of values stored is called the *rank* of the formula. We determine the rank of a formula by counting from right to left. The occurrence of a variable increases the count by one, while each function, except negation, decreases

(Left) The Burroughs Truth Function Evaluator Is Mounted on a 6-Foot Relay Rack and Is Operated by a 50-Volt Power Supply. (Right) The Truth Function Evaluator with Front Covers Removed.

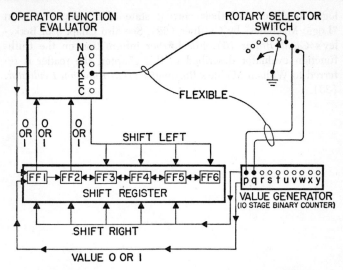

BURROUGHS TRUTH FUNCTION EVALUATOR

the count by one. The running count of this formula has been written above it. Its rank is 3. A well-formed formula always ends up with a count of 1; for there can be no more than one result for any particular evaluation.

The illustration above shows the basic units in the truth-function evaluator. They are (1) a source of values of the variables, (2) a shift register to stack up the variables until evaluated by the operator function evaluator, and (3) a rotary selector switch to scan the formula at the rate of ten symbols per second. The formula to be evaulated is plugged to the stepping switch contacts in the order from right to left as the symbols appear in the formula.

By means of the truth-function evaluator, it is possible to test a tautology of length 98 (ten variables) for every one of its 1024 combinations. By hand this would require making a truth table of 108 columns and 1024 rows. The machine can also compare a reduced or simplified form of a logic with the original, and tell whether or not a correct simplification has been made.

BIBLIOGRAPHICAL NOTE

Jevons describes his logical machine in Chap. 23 of his *Elementary Lessons in Logic* (25). An account of the history of logic machines and their current state of development is in "Logic Machines" by Gardner (22). See also Chap. 9 of Berkeley's *Giant Brains* (5). For further information on the truth-function evaluator described in this chapter, the reader is referred to William Miehle's *Burroughs Truth Function Evaluator.* (33).

General Bibliography

In the following list will be found those books to which references have been made in the text or in bibliographical notes.

1. Ambrose, Alice, and Lazerowitz, Morris, *Fundamentals of Symbolic Logic*, New York, Rinehart and Co., 1948.
2. Aristotle, *Prior Analytics, Posterior Analytics, Metaphysics,* and *On Sophistical Refutations,* in *The Oxford Translation of Aristotle,* ed. J. A. Smith and W. D. Ross, London, Oxford University Press, 1908–1931, 11 vols.
3. Ayer, A. J., *Language, Truth and Logic,* rev. ed., London, Victor Gollancz, 1946.
4. Basson, A. H., and O'Connor, D. J., *Introduction to Symbolic Logic,* London, University Tutorial Press, 1953.
5. Berkeley, Edmond C., *Giant Brains,* New York, John Wiley and Sons, 1949.
6. Black, Max, "The Justification of Induction," in *Language and Philosophy,* Ithaca, Cornell University Press, 1949.
7. Blackburn, P. C., and White, L., eds., *Logical Nonsense,* New York, G. P. Putnam's Sons, 1934.
8. Boole, George, *An Investigation of the Laws of Thought* (1854), Chicago and London, The Open Court Publishing Co., 1940.
9. Chase, Stuart, *Guides to Straight Thinking,* New York, Harper & Brothers, 1956.
10. Churchman, C. West, *Elements of Logic and Formal Science,* Philadelphia, J. B. Lippincott Co., 1940.
11. Cohen, Morris R., and Nagel, Ernest, *An Introduction to Logic and Scientific Method,* New York, Harcourt, Brace and Co., 1934.
12. Cooley, John, *A Primer of Formal Logic,* New York, The Macmillan Company, 1942.
13. De Morgan, Augustus, *Formal Logic,* London, Taylor and Walter, 1847.

14. De Morgan, Augustus, *A Budget of Paradoxes* (1872), New York, Dover Publications, 1954.

15. Dodgson, C. L. ("Lewis Carroll"), *The Game of Logic,* London, Macmillan and Co., 1886.

16. Dodgson, C. L. ("Lewis Carroll"), *Symbolic Logic,* 4th ed., (1897), New York, E. C. Berkeley, 1956.

17. Dodgson, C. L. ("Lewis Carroll"), *The Complete Works of Lewis Carroll,* ed. Alexander Woollcott, New York, Random House, 1937.

18. Dublin, L. I.; Lotka, A. J.; and Spiegelman, M., *Length of Life,* New York, The Ronald Press Co., 1949.

19. Eaton, Ralph M., *General Logic,* New York, Charles Scribner's Sons, 1931.

20. Feigl, H., and Sellars, W., eds., *Readings in Philosophical Analysis,* New York, Appleton-Century-Crofts, 1949.

21. Frankfurter, Felix, *The Case of Sacco and Vanzetti,* Boston, Little, Brown and Co., 1927.

22. Gardner, Martin, "Logic Machines," *Scientific American,* March, 1952.

23. Hempel, C. G., "On the Nature of Mathematical Truth" and "Geometry and Empirical Science," in *Readings in Philosophical Analysis,* ed. H. Feigl and W. Sellars, New York, Appleton-Century-Crofts, 1949.

24. Hume, David, *An Enquiry Concerning Human Understanding* (1748), La Salle, Ill., Open Court Publishing Co., 1935.

25. Jevons, W. Stanley, *Elementary Lessons in Logic* (1870), London, Macmillan and Co., 1928.

26. Johnstone, Henry W., Jr., *Elementary Deductive Logic,* New York, Thomas Y. Crowell Co., 1954.

27. Keynes, John Maynard, *Formal Logic,* 4th ed., London, 1906.

28. Keynes, John Maynard, *A Treatise on Probability* (1921), London, Macmillan and Co., 1952.

29. Langer, Susanne, *An Introduction to Symbolic Logic,* New York, Dover Publications, 1953.

30. Lecomte du Noüy, Pierre, *Human Destiny,* New York, The New American Library, 1949.

31. Mace, C. A., *The Principles of Logic,* New York, and London, Longmans, Green and Co., 1933.

32. Metropolitan Life Insurance Company, *Statistical Bulletin,* June, 1951.

33. Miehle, William, *Burroughs Truth Function Evaluator*, Detroit, Burroughs Corporation, 1955.

34. Mill, John Stuart, *A System of Logic* (1843), London, Longmans, Green and Co., 1925.

35. Nagel, Ernest, "Logic Without Ontology," in *Readings in Philosophical Analysis*, ed. H. Feigl and W. Sellars, New York, Appleton-Century-Crofts, 1949.

36. Nagel, Ernest, and Newman, James R., "Gödel's Proof," *Scientific American*, June, 1956; also in *The World of Mathematics*, ed. James R. Newman, New York, Simon and Schuster, 1956.

37. Pap, Arthur, *Elements of Analytic Philosophy*, New York, The Macmillan Company, 1949.

38. Quine, W. V., "Truth by Convention," in *Readings in Philosophical Analysis*, ed. H. Feigl and W. Sellars, New York, Appleton-Century-Crofts, 1949.

39. Quine, W. V., *Methods of Logic*, New York, Henry Holt and Co., 1950.

40. Quine, W. V., "Two Dogmas of Empiricism," in *From a Logical Point of View*, Cambridge, Mass., Harvard University Press, 1953.

41. Reichenbach, Hans, "The Logical Foundations of Probability" and "The Justification of Induction," in *Readings in Philosophical Analysis*, ed. H. Feigl and W. Sellars, New York, Appleton-Century-Crofts, 1949.

42. Ryle, Gilbert, *Dilemmas*, Cambridge University Press, 1954.

43. Schiller, F. C. S., *Formal Logic*, London, Macmillan and Co., 1931.

44. Shannon, Claude E., "A Symbolic Analysis of Relay and Switching Circuits," Transactions of The American Institute of Electrical Engineers, 1938, vol. 57, pp. 713–723.

45. Strawson, P. F., *Introduction to Logical Theory*, London, Methuen and Co., 1952.

46. Ushenko, A. P., *The Problems of Logic*, London, George Allen and Unwin, 1941.

47. Whitehead, Alfred North, and Russell, Bertrand, *Principia Mathematica* (1910), 2nd ed., Cambridge, Cambridge University Press, 1950, vol. 1.

48. Williams, Donald, *The Ground of Induction*, Cambridge, Mass., Harvard University Press, 1947.

Index

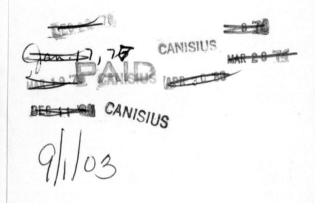